My Man Jack

BAWDY TALES
FROM IRISH FOLKLORE

MICHAEL J. MURPHY

with an Introduction by
BENEDICT KIELY

First published in 1989 by
Brandon Book Publishers Ltd
Dingle, Co. Kerry, Ireland

© Michael J. Murphy 1989

British Library Cataloguing in Publication Data
Murphy, Michael J.
    My man Jack: bawdy tales from Irish folklore.
    1. Irish tales
    I. Title
    398.2'1'09415

    ISBN O-86322-104-1

Cover illustration by Joe Boske
Cover design by Graphiconies, Dublin
Typeset by Irish Typesetting and Publishing, Galway
Printed by Richard Clay Ltd, Bungay

A note on the author

Michael J. Murphy worked as a folklore collector for the former Irish Folklore Commission from 1949 until 1971, and continued in the same capacity from 1971 until his retirement in July 1983 in the Department of Irish Folklore, University College Dublin. More than thirty years of experience in the field yielded some 31,000 pages of typewritten material, much of it transcription of many hundreds of hours of tapes recorded from the people of counties Armagh, Antrim, Cavan, Derry, Down, Fermanagh, Leitrim, Louth, Meath, Monaghan, Sligo and Tyrone. This material covers all aspects of Irish folk culture, ranging from folk narrative to customs, beliefs, social organisations and material folk culture. Indeed, a singularly important aspect of Michael J. Murphy's work was the acquisition of many artefacts for the National Museum of Ireland's Folk Life Collections, and the outstanding help he gave the museum with the task of documenting disappearing traditional crafts.

His numerous newspaper articles and contributions to radio and television programmes, both at home and abroad, have played no small part in bringing a deeper understanding of folklore and the importance of folklore studies to a wider audience. Among his published books are sensitive descriptions of his experience as a collector. The most outstanding among these are *At Slieve Gullion's Foot* and *Tyrone Folk Quest*, as well as works dealing with various genres of folk literature – *Now You're Talking* and, most recently, an edition of his important collections from Rathlin Island, *Rathlin: Island of Blood and Enchantment*. In addition, Michael J. Murphy is well known as a short story writer and playwright.

Over the years material from his folklore collections has

been drawn upon by hundreds of scholars from many countries, while Michael J. Murphy has given generously of his time in assisting and advising groups of students and individual scholars.

Séamas Ó Catháin
Department of Irish Folklore
University College Dublin

Contents

Introduction

In the 1940s Michael J. Murphy went for two years, and on behalf of the Folklore Commission, from his native neighbourhood around Slieve Gullion mountain up into Glenhull, in the Sperrins, in north Tyrone.

About his life and work there he wrote a book: *Tyrone Folk Quest*. A reviewer in a Dublin newspaper, a lady and a dear friend of mine, said that Murphy made as much about travelling that distance as if he had gone to New Zealand. The implication was that there was little difference between south Armagh and north Tyrone. But there was and, I feel, there still may be.

Certainly in the 1940s before TV, the great leveller, came to stay and when, because of the war, the motor cars were scarce on the road, the differences were quite striking even if one needed a subtle man like Michael to point them out. Here he is, approaching the Sperrins on that quest for folklore in Tyrone:

> Far ahead the Sperrins cowered. My instinct anticipated rain, and much as I was enjoying this company and the spin I tried to persuade them to return. Neither wore coats. I prophesied a deluge.

When the rain began they [i.e. his two companions for the day] said it would be a passing shower. To me, it was to be, as we'd say in south Armagh, "long-tailed and heavy". So it was. We sat first under a tree, I talking of folklore I had collected, making comments, relating it to the vanishing life of the countryside. The tree began to drip and we took shelter in a wee house where we were welcomed by a small, decent Orange-woman who wanted to make tea for us . . .

Long after with rain still falling we parted, they for Omagh, myself for the overcast country of Munterloney, Greencastle and Glenhull . . .

But he noted that one of his companions of that day remembered the occasion and, afterwards, wrote about it. In this fashion:

The tumult of the passing of the youngsters on their way to a Mission in the local church at Killyclogher aroused and inspired our companion, Michael Murphy, and he began to speak. He treated us to a long talk on the history and the ground of Ireland, the ways of her people, the folk tradition and, in the end, he came to the destiny of our young people in the world we live in today.

He was informative and most moving, and suddenly I thought: this man here beside me is a druid, as much a part of this ancient land as the stone he sits on. He could have been here on this hillside under this oak before Patrick came. For such close wisdom could come only from centuries of meditation . . . A druid from the land around Fionn Mac Cumhaill's mountain in south Armagh.

That now was me quoting myself about my first meeting with Michael Murphy, away more than forty years ago. Even though what I then wrote did lead to Michael getting serious letters from people in the States who thought that he was a practising druid, (whatever in hell or heaven or under the oak a druid practises), I think it was fair comment and that it still stands. I also remember that on that notable day the orange lilies were in all their glory before the wee house in which the wee Orange-woman offered to make tea for Michael, my brother-in-law, Frank McCrory, and myself. It was coming up to the Twelfth.

Faraor Géar! When will such a happy invitation be given again?

My first knowledge of Michael Murphy was through his first book, *At Slieve Gullion's Foot*. It was described very modestly by its first publisher as "a countryman's book about his own countryside at the foot of one of the famous mountains of Ireland". A modest claim, indeed, for the book and for the mountain that guards the Gap of the North and is alive with legend and is one of the seven holy mountains of Ireland; and on the summit of which A.E. (possibly) met Fionn Mac Cumhaill; and on the slopes of which George Moore, on a warm day, swapped his long drawers for a glass of milk provided by a "chance shepherd".

That first book, though, changed Michael's way of life. It brought him a letter from Dr Séamas Delargy of the Folklore Commission asking him to join the staff of folklore collectors. Thereafter he became a man who, as some decent rural people thought, followed the fairies and, more remarkably still, made a living out of it. That was a notion by no means confined to simple people and rural places. In its early days, and in allegedly educated quarters, the Folklore Commission could be regarded as a group of benighted people intent on reviving ancient superstition almost up to the point of, like the nuns in Honor Tracy's novel, leaping through the fire on Midsummer Eve.

That, as we all now know, was not the case.

But Michael Murphy, as his first book revealed and as Delargy immediately saw, had a natural gift for intently observing and noting down the way of life of people on the land. In the introduction to a later book, *Ulster Folk of Field and Fireside*, he declared his gratitude to Delargy's cultural vision which, he said, introduced him to a way of life that became for him, for over forty years, both challenge and vocation. And he also wrote:

> Indebted, too, must be the social historians and students of folklife studies for the hundreds of volumes I have contributed to the archives of the Department of Irish Folklore in UCD. Because I know I have written one of the greatest, if not *the* greatest, stories to have come out of Ulster. I can make that claim unblushingly. Apart from my journals they represent the story of the people told by the people themselves for the first and, no doubt, for the last time.

That was a humorous and modest boast. It was also an exact statement.

And while Michael Murphy, the collector, was hard at work from Blacklion to Ballycastle and from Forkhill to Limavady, Michael the writer was coming up with short stories, articles, radio talks, stage-plays. A busy druid.

Herein he gives us some laughable and lighter products of his intense gathering: little nuggets that the greedy and careless panhandler might have trodden on and left neglected in the gravel by the stream. They are light and laughable and bred into the bone of decent country people. He refers to a collection of somewhat similar stories from the Ozark mountains, a copy of which collection I possess and enjoy.

But here and now I refer to another and a greater collection. How many stories in this style did the Canterbury pilgrims tell to each other?

Well, perhaps not all of the pilgrims.

Benedict Kiely

For Kevin, Maureen and Derek

Preface

If the following tales amuse or cause outright laughter then they will have fulfilled their traditional purpose, as they did for generations of our foreparents who listened to the tales told in the fields where they worked or around the firesides at night, in forges or at wakes. Our foreparents heard the tales told, and often told by skilled storytellers, but not read. No folk-tale was meant to be printed; a tale which has to be read loses such qualities as emphasis, repetition, the pause and modulation of voice, and facial and other gestures.

Such tales may still be regarded, despite modern liberalism in diction, as containing matter of indelicate expression, but in no way did the people look on them as either "dirty" or pornographic. The traditional intent of the bawdy tale was to give healthy amusement and laughter in mixed company, in an honest expression of an impulse derived from a ubiquitous human instinct. Much the same impulse may be claimed for the pornographic, but there is a fundamental distinction between the two: the bawdy tale is extrovert and outgoing, the other is introvert and sly; the bawdy does not exult in the sexual content of its myths, the pornographic does nothing else. The bawdy can uplift in its mirth, the other arouses a smirk of suppressed guilt, is solitary and bound to be degrading.

I myself began as a collector proper with the Irish Folklore Commission, collecting tales in the Ulster counties and in counties Louth, Leitrim, Roscommon, Sligo and Mayo. In due course the oral heritage I collected was submitted, in typeform, to the archivist of the Irish Folklore Commission, Dr Séan O'Sullivan, who surprised me by writing, "I am glad that you included the risqué ones, as sensitive collectors might be liable to let them go unrecorded on account of their content. Still, they are part of the pattern and should be noted." Though I collect folktales mainly in the northern counties, these tales also form part of the general body of Irish folklore. The locations of the stories vary, of course, as do the styles of narration, but the theme, the motif, and the denouement stay the same. For example, one story from County Mayo is located on Croagh Patrick, while its kindred tale takes place at a lake in County Down. In one a boy and girl "climb the reek" out of season; in the other a couple make rounds of the lake on their knees. In both stories the couples are understood to be making a public confession of the sin of fornication.

The northern dialect created problems for me at first. In the early 1950s, at my first Lammas Fair in Ballycastle in County Antrim, I was standing in a crowded bar while my companion, Hugh Dillon, a native of the town, left to go to the toilet. Beside me stood two men deep in conversation and amid the babble of voices the only word I could understand was "ewes". Suddenly the taller of the two craggy faced men hollered to the barmaid: "Hi-ye, cuttie, gay us two hay-yins o' scaw het!" He had spoken his order fast and turned to resume his conversation with his crony.

The girl behind the bar blushed. She leaned towards me

and said, "Excuse me, sir, but could you tell me what that man ordered?"

I could not. She blushed deeper and said that this was her first day in the bar and her very first time in the North!

Meanwhile the sheepman turned and, finding his order had not been set up on the bar, glared at the girl and repeated, "Cuttie, I tult ye: gay us two hay-yins o' scaw het," and he went back to his discussion about ewes.

The barmaid's face was now on fire. Meanwhile, however, Hugh Dillon had returned and seen her embarrassment. He advised her, "The man said, 'Young girl, I told you to give us two half-ones of Scotch, hot'."

When I went gathering tales in the Glenhull district of County Tyrone older people would sometimes remark at my approach, "So, it's the old rehearsals you're after". As well as understanding local dialect and accent, building a relationship with people took time and trust. I collected tales from labourers, small farmers, sheepmen, publicans, ex-policemen; from pedlars and seamen, blacksmiths and housewives. Stories were told by the narrator's fireside or in the snug or kitchen of a pub; I sought integration and closeness with the teller, and we spoke in the local idiom. However, though everyone has a story just a few people can be called storytellers. Philip Dolan, a robust, active man until his death at the age of 80, was typical of those who had this gift. He loved talk and to talk of the folklore of his native area, and as he spoke he would shape his stories with imaginative description and colourful traditional phrases. He was one of the best narrators I have ever met and, like all really good storytellers, he had a phenomenal memory. Sometimes also this talent would run in families, just as musical ability does. I heard the tale, "The Cattle Dealer and the Parson", from a companion, the late Ned McCrink, who had probably heard it from his father, John, or a relative, Mickey McCrink of Ballinamada. The McCrinks were a family in the parish noted, in fact, both for their storytelling and their singing. Stories and story-tellers emerged from the countryside and blended in with it, and this *dúchas* the folklorist was obliged to respect.

By contrast, I heard the following story in the 1960s in Clonduff parish in County Down. An American sociology student was interested in bachelors and heard that four brothers lived together on the farm they worked in the hill country of Lecale, County Down. Their parents were dead and there was no woman in the family. The four seemed to offer a fine source of information for a sex survey. The American drove to the laneway, or "lunnin", to the farm, left his car and walked up to the house. The brothers were finishing a meal in the kitchen and, when the American explained, obliquely, what he was after they invited him in. He had some difficulty with their Scots-sounding accent so the talk was slow and, as with all country people, the brothers were more suspicious than curious. Eventually, however, he mentioned the word itself: sex.

One brother acted as speaker. "Ach, we have it bare in the loft all winter," he informed the visitor.

The American couldn't believe his ears: they were surprisingly frank, even casual about the topic.

"They tell me it germinates better when rested," the brother continued.

The American was flabbergasted. He had not found such unashamed frankness even in the far south of his own hill country in the USA. However, he was puzzled also by the northern accent, but before he could voice his uncertainty the other declared, "Ach, we don't bother with secks until early spring. We sell what we can and leave the rest bare for seed and ourselves."

At this point the American student explained that his survey had nothing to do with "sacks" of corn, and gave a few details of what he actually had in mind. The four brothers stiffened. Then as one man they rose in their wrath and reached for whatever weapons they could lay their hands on. The sociology student fled.

While I collected folklore that was concerned with life and humour generally, I found that within that broad category there were special difficulties in collecting any folklore involving sex. One needed to be sensitive to the concerns of the storyteller and to remain aware of the differences in local phrasing. In south Armagh a girl who had an illegitimate child would have "met with a mistake", while in County Cavan she would have "made a slip" or "come with the heat of a shower". When a man I knew was asked if his wife was "a good court" he replied, "I don't know what you mean by a good court, but she bellies up right and fine".

For all their earthiness country people had reason to be cautious about sex. The churches propounded and to some extent enforced a narrow, repressive theology of sexuality. They were particularly harsh on women. Women who had illegitimate children were subjected to public punishment; the community was warned to treat them as outcasts and they were put on display as sinners in the churches. In the Church of Ireland a woman who had sinned sexually was made to stand outside the church door after Service while the congregation filed past; in the Catholic Church women had to stand in the aisle during Mass, dressed in a white smock. Sometimes, too, women were driven out of the confessional in tears, without absolution.

Local priests everywhere dispersed couples courting, and broke up dances in the houses and at the crossroads. Redemptorists, in particular, were obsessed with what they called "company keeping" and one missioner was so outraged at the practice of courting on Wednesdays and Sundays that he denounced it with the cry, "Once a week to God, twice a week to the devil!" All dancing was said by the Catholic clergy to be immoral. In the 1890s the priests broke up dances with their blackthorn sticks. My mother remembered one such occasion when her sister and her sister's boyfriend, together with two others, sought refuge from the priest in a pig sty. They crouched ankle deep in pig dung as the priest rattled his stick off the sty shouting that he would "put horns on them". Fear of the priest persisted into this century and the sight of one was often enough to rout a gathering of dancers, scattering them "like hens before a strange cat". In the 1930s the parish priest of Dromantee claimed that with his fast car he had emptied every "courting den" in the parish. To this the late Peter Babe replied, "Father, you only drove them behind the ditches where you can't see them".

Though the Church did much to repress the peasantry's cultural, social and sexual expression, the people were by no means downtrodden. When the parish priest of Kiloury, County Louth, broke up a dance in a local big house and threw the musician's accordeon into the fire, he was told off sharply by one of the young men present. Not everyone would stand for the priest interfering in their affairs. In my own area of Dromantee the curate went to reprimand a young girl for having had an illegitimate child. "Leave me alone, Father," she snapped at him, "or I won't quit till I have them running as thick as the rabbits on Slieve Gullion." The priests, too, were often quite removed from people's lives and were in any case ignorant of many of their customs and traditions. A man from Crossmaglen in County Armagh who had been "throwing mobs" at wakes went deliberately to the new priest in his parish to confess his sin, hoping to get off with a light penance. As it turned out, the priest had no idea as to what he was confessing.

Mobbing was a term used to denote the practice once common at wakes of exchanging uninhibited satirical and sarcastic repartee in a contest of wit. A "good mobber" was one noted for the depth of sarcasm and cutting satire in his ripostes: if weak or ineffective he – no women appear to have taken part in this risky custom – might be told to "take his cutty from among the spoons". Sometimes two gifted individuals were left to make the contest between them. Friends or relatives of either of the contestants might throw in a riposte, and their help was welcomed. These helpers would always be neighbours or relatives so that the contest became one between two townlands or territorial areas. Occasionally a mob might be so cutting and offensive that it would incense the other party: a row would break out, and the Church, once again, would call for an end to be put to wakes.

No longer does the hierarchy condemn wakes and wake games or songs, though until their passing in the mid-'40s the Church in synod and in pastorals had for at least four centuries denounced them.[1] The Church condemned wake games as being pagan in origin, which they undoubtedly were, though no one taking part was aware of such a stigma. The old people did not want a quiet wake and said so; they took such as indicating a slur on the corpse. However, no wake game was played over the death of a young person or a person who had met a sudden death, or if some "friend of the corpse" objected. Otherwise games were played in the wake house kitchen, or a barn, with the corpse in view. The wake games, like the bawdy tales, had ribald connotations. The names given to the men and young men who took part in them had a bawdy if oblique reference to the sexual act. One such game was that called "My Man Jack"; another, "Rose o' Roses, I'm in Love", had a similar formula, the names being traditional and heard only at wakes.

Take the game of "My Man Jack". Players sat here and there in the throng in the wake house until one man, a sort of master of ceremonies, suggested a game. He ungirthed a stout leather belt, or was loaned one, and appointed a quick-witted man as "Jack". These two then went through the crowd giving names to each person taking part. They ran like this: Piss agin the wind; Meely-mouth-a-tubber-guts; Stop the tide with a pitchfork, and so on. The names were sarcastic and satirical, some were traditional and others were coined by some affair connected with the person which he would prefer to avoid speaking of – this heightened the laughter of course. With names doled out to each player, the belt man began: "The priest of the parish has lost his considering cap; some say this and some say that, and I say my man Jack."

The game moved rapidly now.

"Me sir?" said Jack.

"Yes, you sir."

"You're a liar sir."

"Who then sir?"

"The priest himself."

"Me sir?"

"Yes, you sir."

"You're a liar sir."

"Who then sir?"

"Piss agin the wind. Piss agin the wind."

The player in the crowd so named then replied smartly:

"Me sir?"

"Yes, you sir."

"You're a liar sir."

"Who then sir?"

"High up and hard to get at."

So the game went on, and if a player were slow in answering or answered wrongly he was slapped with the belt. Each player named the next: Shinowore's shift; Piss agin the wind; High up and hard to get at; Scud me through the whins; Barney Marmion's push-pole; Hart's Jack; Belly of champ; Rattle me fart in a can.

The sexual connotations are obvious but some may also require a word of explanation. "Whins" meant gorse or furze while "scud" could mean courtship. The push-pole, a length of timber used to haul a threshing mill, referred, in this context, to the penis. "Hart's Jack" referred to the jack-ass: at night groups of young fellows had the jack-ass cover asses and ponies – the owners, it need hardly be said, were not amused.

Although tradition tells that singing and dancing took place at wakes in earlier times, in recent years singing was only heard at the wake game we knew as "Marrying Out".[2] In "Marrying Out" – the only game in which a woman might take part, and here she remained silent – a girl was taken from the room where the women sat chatting and, often reluctantly, brought by two belt men to a chair in the kitchen among the men and boys. The two men had already picked out one unmarried man and the girl was told to select another young man from the crowd. This made a complement of four men, with a belt man between each of the other two. Then the man named as the "True Priest" commenced the game. The four moved slowly around the girl and the first man called out was ordered to sing. If the song was "longsome" in coming the belt man whacked him on the back with the belt and if he pleaded that he couldn't sing he was belted again until he did, or else "left his stick" on someone in the crowd who sang for him. Then, after the first man had finished, the second one was called on to sing. When that song ended there were cries of "True Priest, True Priest!"

The "True Priest" (perhaps another indicative term) was a traditional character, a local as all were. He was a man noted for his uninhibited speech, his scathing remarks and wit. He knew everyone and what he did know of the girl's love life and the boy's, or perhaps their parents' objections to a marriage match, he told, and these he referred to taking the theme of the songs as his pivot. At length he refused to accept the songs as being unfit "to give the girl to any of them, so let us have the songs long and strong again", and so a second and third song were sung. After further cutting remarks based on the songs, which the listeners enjoyed while the girl hung her head in embarrassment, the "True Priest" gave one of the men to her. She fled the room as one of the young men dived among the throng. The survivor named another girl, and so the game began again.

The game was originally a fertility ritual, its inner and pagan motif long since lost. A cousin of mine, the late

Sister Benedicta, told of an experience a sister nun had on a South Sea island. She had witnessed a fertility ritual held in the open which was almost identical to our game of "Marrying Out". The presence of the corpse was important: the dead person was seeing life propagating and continuing. This viewpoint had the support of the Christian ethic as well as the traditional belief, but no folklorists can give the origin for the wake and the wake game in identical terms.

The professional view regarding the decline of the wake and the wake game is that a more sophisticated attitude towards rural amusement developed among country people, fed by the local paper and the radio. The war-time scarcity of rations and the decline in the use of clay pipes further inhibited the holding of wakes. At a wake, every person taking a pipe from the dish of a galvanised bucket murmured, "Lord have mercy on the dead" (hence the expression "Lord o' mercy pipes"). Cigarettes were no real substitute in this tradition. Traditionally also there were two nights of waking with burial at three o'clock on the third day. Due to the war scarcities this was reduced to one night of waking, with the corpse removed to the church the next evening, followed by Mass and burial around midday on the third day. Wake games continued in outlying parts of south Armagh and County Down until the mid-'40s but have now completely disappeared as a pattern.

The same changes in the life of rural communities throughout Ireland have led to a decline, too, in the telling of tales such as are recorded here. Working on the bog cutting turf or in the meadow saving hay were great occasions for storytelling; one man would tell a story and then another would follow, and the tales and yarns would continue while the *meitheal* worked together. In this way, too, tales would be carried from one district to another by farm labourers and journeymen. However, traditional work patterns changed: more and more people left the land as agriculture became consolidated in bigger farm units, while increased mechanisation reduced the amount of people needed to work the farms. New practices, such as the introduction of the Agricultural Employment Acts, did away with the traditional hiring fairs, while the old trades and occupations went into decline also. Where once the day in the fields and the night by the fireside were shortened by the telling of tales of many kinds, now few work the fields together and the television set has taken over as the centre of attention in people's homes. We have lost much of the cultural self-sufficiency of earlier generations but we can, nevertheless, recall and enjoy the vibrancy and wit of those "old rehearsals".

This compilation of tales came about by chance. When collecting material in County Cavan I met an American and his wife who had heard of me and wanted to learn about folklore. I talked on the subject into the small hours. In appreciation of the visit they sent me Vance Randolph's collection of bawdy tales from the Ozark Mountains in Arkansas, *Pissing in the Snow*. Like my tales the Randolph stories were short and, when Professor Bo Almqvist suggested that I check how many of the Randolph tales were relevant to my own collection, I was surprised to find that more than 40 of Randolph's 101 tales held similarities to mine. No research has been done to explain the strength of this connection, but as a guide to further study in this area I have indexed Frank A. Hoffman's annotation of the Randolph stories where they are relevant to the tales collected here. The tales noted are marked in the text with an asterisk.

The method of presenting the tales is my own. Some I wrote in longhand during the course of an interview and typed up later; other tales were tape recorded, and the tapes and their transcription are now in the archives of the Department of Folklore at University College Dublin.

Storytellers never titled their tales, and the titles given here are my own.

My thanks are due to Dr Séamas Ó Catháin, Archivist to the Department of Irish Folklore, who read the book in typescript, and to Bairbre Ó Fhloinn who did research and copying in the archives in Dublin. My thanks also to the editor of *Ulster Folklife* who published my story entitled "The Amadthon" and added annotations to it; and especially to Frank A. Hoffman, Professor of English at the State University of Buffalo, New York, for permission to use his annotation of *Pissing in the Snow*, and to the late Vance Randolph of Arkansas who compiled the aforementioned collection. Special thanks are due to Professor Bo Almqvist, head of the Department of Irish Folklore in University College Dublin, for offering suggestions which led to this volume being compiled and for his kind permission to allow me to publish the tales.

1. A detailed account is given in Seán Ó Súilleabháin, *Irish Wake Games*, Mercier 1967.
2. Seán Ó Súilleabháin lists scores of names for this game in his monumental work, *A Handbook of Irish Folklore*, the Educational Company of Ireland 1942.

The Age of Innocence

The Oul' Bugger

A group of men from Lurgancanty set off to seek work in Scotland; with them was a young man of retarded growth and with a fresh complexion who, although looking like a boy, was almost as old as any of the others. Having secured work they looked for lodgings and found a land-lady who was, as it happened, constricted for space and beds. She said two would have to sleep in each bed in the rooms and, as to the "wee fellow", he could sleep with her own young daughter.

After supper the Scotswoman hushed her daughter off to bed and ordered the wee lad to go along with her, and the others sat around smoking and talking for a while. Suddenly they heard an alarmed cry from the top of the stairs: "Mither! He's an oul' bugger!"

Taken down in the 1960s in Lurgancanty, County Down.

The Man for Me

One wild, stormy night three men called to a house to seek shelter. The woman of the house made them welcome and gave them food, and then offered them a bed to share between them. When the men retired to bed the mother sat by the fire in the kitchen with her daughter, a single girl she was eager to see married. As the storm outside worsened they overheard one of the men lament, "All my fine cattle and sheep out in a storm on a night like this. They'll be lost!"

"That," whispered the mother to her daughter, "is the man for you."

But just then they heard the second man complain, "But what about my fine ships on the sea of a night like this? They'll all be lost."

"No," whispered the mother again, "there's the man for you!"

Now the third man called out to the man beside him in the bed, "Move over, you're lying on me tool."

"I am not," replied the other.

"Then if it's not you it's the fellow beyond you."

"No, mother," said the girl, *"there's* the man for me!"

Versions of this tale were told to me in Dromantee parish and in other areas of old Ulster (which included the counties Louth and Meath now in the province of Leinster). This version was recorded in 1973 in Blacklion, County Cavan.*

Virginity in Jeopardy

Two old sisters and a cousin, all spinsters, lived together in a small house at Moyra Castle in the Gap of the North in Dromantee parish. At that time, the 1930s, the spirit of hospitality was observed according to tradition. One very wet night a travelling woman called and asked for shelter; the travelling woman was a common sight and was given food and shelter for a night or two as she passed through the countryside. The spinsters invited the traveller to stay, as was the custom. It rained heavily the next day and on the following morning, a Sunday, the sisters and cousin got up early to prepare to go to Mass in Dromantee. Having no toilet they went outside to urinate and one of them noticed the travelling woman a little further on, selecting a spot along a high wall. The travelling woman took an upright stance and drew out "her" penis: it was a man in woman's clothing. The spinsters screamed, and he fled.

On their way to Mass the three women told of their experience with horror and apprehension. One remarked, "Hadn't we some poor body's blessin' an' the grace of God he didn't go round us all!"

Recounted to me in Dromantee parish, County Armagh. Many tales are told of men who dressed in women's clothing and went about as travellers to tramp the roads.

Wart and All

A girl who was about to be married was behaving very anxiously, but she would not tell her mother what was bothering her. The boy's parents too knew that she was worried, but she would not tell them either. So the boy's father decided that they should try to find out what was upsetting the girl. He dressed himself in woman's clothes and went one night to the girl's house claiming to be a travelling woman looking for a night's shelter. The girl's family made the travelling woman welcome and said she could share the bed with the girl for the night. Eventually all went to their rooms.

Once she had been in bed for a while the girl began to sigh and sigh, and the traveller asked her what ailed her. At first the girl refused to tell, so the traveller said that she might be able to help. Her own family, she said, were "up and doing for themselves, pushing their own fortune through the world," but her husband had died, she had grown lonely, and in the end "took to the high road".

The girl had heard that travelling women knew a lot and were very resourceful people, and on hearing the woman's story she decided to tell her secret. She had, she said, a wart growing on her private parts and she was worried that it would anger the boy and prevent her from having a family.

"Let me feel the wart," said the travelling woman.

The girl did so, and then the woman said, "That's nothing to worry about. Feel the wart I have on my privates."

The girl put her hand down to the traveller's crotch. "Oh," she exclaimed, "sure that's the father and mother of all warts!"

Collected in Annerverna, Ravendale, County Louth.

A Disappointed Wife

These two got married, and the usual thing that time was that after the couple would be a month married the daughter would go back to spend a month with her mother. So anyway, this girl went back, worked away with the mother, and after the month was up the mother said to her, "Are you going back now?"

"I am not," said the daughter.

"But your time is up, you should be going back to your husband. Didn't you marry him?"

"Oh, I did," said the girl, "I married him all right; but I'm not going back to him."

"Well tell me this now," said her mother, "did you fall out?"

"We did not," replied the daughter, "we are as friendly as could be."

"And what in the wide world, Mary, is wrong?"

"Ah, now," the girl hedged, "I don't like to tell you mother."

"Ach, could you not tell your own mother? Whatever could it be?"

"Well," said the girl finally, "I suppose I might as well tell you. In the house there's a big double bed; any two people could sleep in it quite comfortable and have plenty of space. But that won't do him – he has to be on top of me. No, I'm definitely not going back; devil the one yard I'll go to him."

Recorded in 1974 in Blacklion, County Cavan.*

The White Calf

A farmer and his young son set out in search of a white calf which had strayed and got lost. When night overtook them they sought shelter in a barn until morning, and as they settled down the father cautioned the boy not to make any noise. However, later in the night a young couple came into the barn, waking the young boy as they began to enjoy sex play. Seeing the girl's private parts her partner exclaimed, "God, I can see the whole world!"

Unable to restrain his anxiety the boy cried out, "Do you happen to see our white calf?"

I first heard this tale in Dromantee in the 1920s and since then have come across other versions all over Ulster. This version was recorded in Blacklion, County Cavan.*

What the Tailor Did Not Make

Years ago the boys used to wear petticoats till they'd be ten or eleven years and more. This particular fellow had never had a pair of trousers, but he used to wear a long overcoat over his petticoats. He got a notion for a girl and he'd go along an odd night to see her, and anyway this night he thought it was time he got a pair of trousers for himself. He went to the tailor and got a pair of trousers made, and the first night wearing them he set off to see the girl. Of course, he had the overcoat on too.

Going along, he had, as we say, to go behind the ditch. He was so unused to the trousers that when he went through his performance he took them off altogether and when he was finished he forgot to put them back on. Off he went with the big, long coat covering him. He met the girl and they chatted together, and when they said goodnight he wondered that she didn't pass some remark on his new trousers. He got indignant about it and said, "Do you notice anything different with me the night?"

"No," she answered.

So he took a few steps back and opened the top button of his coat. "Do you notice anything now?"

"No," said the girl.

He opened another button. "Now?"

"No."

He opened the coat. "Notice anything now?"

"Aye," she said.

"Tailor made them," said the boy.

Recorded in 1979 in Wheathill, County Fermanagh.

The Obedient Son

A young man lived with his father, a widower, in a remote and backward part of the mountain where they worked a small farm and tended some sheep. Each night when the work was done and the supper eaten, father and son sat around the open hearth, their boots off, and smoked their clay pipes. When it grew late the father would put aside his pipe in a hole in the wall above the hob, light a candle, and lead the way to the bedroom where he and his son slept together. However, one night the father said he felt it was time the son was looking for a woman, that is, for a wife.

"Whatever you say, da," agreed the son.

So the father went around the district with a matchmaker and found a girl who consented to marry the son. There was an unused room in the house and this was prepared for the bridal couple. The marriage took place, a wedding dance was held and, there being no thought of honeymoons in those days, the "new woman" came straight to her husband's house. That night she went to bed in the room while, as usual, her husband sat smoking at the fireside with his father.

Putting his pipe aside and lighting the candle the father said it was time for bed and headed for the room. The son was soon at his heels. At the door of the room the father realised that the son was following as usual and turned and stopped him. "No, no, no," he said, "you have to go from this out to the other room and sleep with her."

"Sleep with a strange woman!" cried the son in shock.

"Now listen," the father soothed him, "when I was married I had to sleep with your mother."

"But that was ma," said the son. "Anyone could sleep with ma."

Eventually, however, the father persuaded his son to go to the other room and sleep with the "new woman".

The woman took over the household chores but as time went by she showed a snappish temper which puzzled the old man. Eventually he asked her was their anything wrong. "It's this man of mine," she answered, "he knows nothing."

The father said he would speak to his son about this when they sat at the fire that night and later, when they had been smoking for a while, the father brought up the matter of the woman's bad temper. He explained to the son that a man had a certain duty to perform when in bed with his wife, and that he should attend to it.

The son jumped to his feet. "See that," he exclaimed, "if

there's a dirty job to be done round this house I always get it!"

I heard this tale told in County Fermanagh and in my native parish of Dromantee. This version is as I heard it in Fermanagh.*

The Handy Woman Handles a Curious Husband

A handy woman was attending a woman in labour at her first confinement. The woman was married to an over-curious but disingenuous man who, because of his curious nature, had stayed at home intent on seeing what would happen at the birth. He was continually going in and out of the room where the wife lay until in the end the handy woman hit on a plan to keep him out of her way. She handed him a bucket and told him to hurry to the well for water and hustled him out of the room. He rushed off and when he returned the handy woman took the full bucket from him, handed him an empty one, and told him to go again to the well. As soon as he had gone the handy woman emptied the bucket through the back window. When he returned he was handed the empty bucket and sent to the well again, and again and again until the child was born.

Later, when he was back at work, a companion failed to turn up one morning; the boss explained that he had stayed at home because his wife was being confined.

"He's in for a sore time today on the water so," advised the curious man.

The handy woman was the untrained, unpaid precursor of the midwife. Stories on a variety of themes are told about her and her resourcefulness but the above is a version of a tale I heard almost everywhere I collected folklore.

Cramps

At a hiring fair in the North an aged woman hired a servant boy who gave his name as Cramps and she brought him back to the farm. Less than a week later the household were all in bed, each in a separate room, when suddenly there was a cry from the old lady's granddaughter, "Grandmother, Cramps is on me! Cramps is on me!"

Snug in her own bed the woman called back, "Stretch your legs, a-wamee."

I have met with versions of this tale in almost every area; elsewhere the injunction from the old woman advises, "Waggle your bum, a-wamee". A-wamee is a phonetic rendering of an Irish term of endearment for a young girl. This version was recorded in Blacklion, County Cavan, in 1977, and in Wheathill, County Fermanagh, in 1979.*

Filling the House

A couple lived on the hillside in Glendun, and some time after they were married the wife was confined in labour expecting the birth of their first baby. The husband was one of those curious men and by sitting on a stool at the kitchen fire could lean back and see into the head of the room where his wife lay in bed. The midwife was there also in attendance.

Suddenly the midwife rushed down to him in alarm and said a complication seemed to have occurred and to fetch the doctor. When the doctor arrived and heard what the midwife had to say he immediately threw off his jacket, and the husband, looking into the room, could see that the doctor seemed to be shaking the woman in labour vigorously. Next thing the midwife, with face flushed and sweat on her brow, hurried into the kitchen and placed a newborn infant on the husband's lap. She returned to the room and left the husband holding the child with some trepidation.

In a short time the midwife was back with another infant and landed this one also on his lap before dashing back to the room again. In real alarm now the man leaned back and looked towards the head of the room: the doctor still seemed to be shaking his wife. When the midwife came out with a third baby the husband called into the room in panic, "Quit shaking her, damn you, before you fill the house!"

Collected in the mid-1950s in Layde, Cushendall, County Antrim.

Adultery and All That Blast

Confession boxes had a simple drapery between the penitent confessing to the priest and the penitents waiting outside who queued close to the confessional while they waited for their turn. Because of this it was not unusual for the people outside to overhear confessions, especially if the priest was old and ordered the penitent to speak up. On this occasion two women next in line for confession heard the priest exclaim in outrage, "You committed adultery!" As the confessor left the box one of the women asked the other, "What's adultery?"

"Fartin'," she answered.

In goes the first woman much troubled in conscience. She confessed to the priest that she had committed adultery. Again the priest burst in outrage, demanding, "When did this happen? How many times?"

"Well, Father," she said, "after I get up maybe, an' rakin' the fire, gettin' the breakfast, feedin' the hens and ducks, throwin' a bit to the pigs, goin' to the well ..."

This tale was told in the 1930s in the Dromantee parish area. Versions of the tale also appear in County Cavan and elsewhere. In Carricknagrow, Blacklion, I heard the same story but with a different end line: after confessing to adultery the priest asks the woman if she is married, and she admits that she is. The priest then asks her what her husband thinks of this behaviour. "He doesn't know," the woman replies, "when I feel it coming I put me arse over the edge of the bed and he never hears it."*

Do Her Heart Good

An old woman had two goats, one of which was fairly aged. The rutting season arrived and at this time, as they phrased it, "the goats were looking away". Unable to travel with the goats to the buck she asked a neighbour if he would bring them, and he agreed to call for the animals on his way from work that evening. He did so, and found that the old woman had tied the aged goat to the young one by the neck. The man said that she was being foolish, that the old goat could not be expected to conceive and have a kid at her age. The woman replied, "I know she can't, but sure won't it do her oul' heart good?"

A popular short tale told by storytellers at fireside céilís in Dromantee parish, County Armagh, in the 1930s.

Urine Had Its Uses

Human urine was used for many purposes and, as well as having a practical value, it also had superstitions attached to it. Touched on horses or cattle for sale it was said to counter the evil influence of either man or witch; at the same time it was used by women as a hairwash, like shampoo. Its main use, however, was in cloth processing where it helped to swell the tightly woven fibres in webs of cloth before the web would be offered for sale. To "thicken the cloth" or "kick the web", as home processes were known, a shallow trough of stones and clay were erected on a kitchen or barn floor and urine, soft soap and hot water was poured into it, saturating the cloth. Neighbouring men and women worked together and, in their bare feet, kicked and pushed the web around the trough. It was hard, nasty work.

In the Glens of Antrim urine was collected in a tub set in the dark spot below the kitchen door and every member of the family, as well as neighbours calling in, were expected to contribute their share to the tub, unless they had eaten apples or onions during the day: these juices passed through the kidneys and contaminated the natural properties of ammonia and alkalides in the urine. In most areas this natural product was collected in barrels from the tenantry and hauled by horse and cart to the tuck mills, and inevitably the drawer was known as "the piss man". When home weaving died out in the 1880s the milling also ceased.

Urine was referred to as chamber-lye or chamber-lee, and though other euphemistic terms were used chamber-lye was the most common. Urine found its way into the local vernacular in such sayings as "You daren't piss here but everyone hears the splash", to denote an area rife with gossips; or a gossip might be dismissed with the disparaging, "She couldn't hold her piss".

How to Boil an Egg in an Emergency

One very warm day in the Highlands of Scotland Kearney was travelling on foot, carrying his pedlar's or pahvee's pack full of cloth. All the rivers and burns had dried up and he was very thirsty. At length he noticed a thin skein of smoke rising behind a hill, and walking in that direction he came on a croft. There was one old woman inside and she welcomed him in Scots Gaelic which he understood because at that time Dromantee had many native speakers of Irish Gaelic. He said he would like a drink because he was dead with the drought, but she said she had no milk of any kind and no water either: her son was a shepherd for the laird and did not return home with water from the spring far back in the hills until evening. "But," she added, "I can boil you an egg."

"How can you do that?" Kearney asked, "seeing as you have no water."

"Well," she replied, "if an old woman couldn't make as much water as would boil an egg ..."

Heard in the early 1930s in Dromantee parish, County Armagh.*

The Long Drip

Along the road near Glenhull stood an old public house and, as in all public houses then, the toilet behind the pub comprised countless acres of rough pasture and rising mountainy ground. The men (no women would then enter a pub) used a spot at the gable of the house beside which a mountain stream emptied through a chute of wood which acted as a pipe or conduit to supply the domestic water. It was the dry season and just a bare trickle dripped continuously from the pipe, forming a little pool on the ground.

A neighbouring man had been to the fair of Ballinascreen ten or more miles away in County Derry. He had sold well and had drunk half-ones of whiskey and pints of porter so that, by the time he had walked to the old pub, he needed further refreshment to revive the alcohol already aboard. He then went out to relieve himself at the dripping pipe. He was a long time gone when suddenly those inside heard a cry: "For God's sake some of yous come out! Get me a doctor: I'm running away in water!"

Heard in the early 1950s in Carnanrancy, Greencastle parish, County Tyrone.

Going to Have a Child

A doctor attended a man who was ill and directed that a sample of the patient's urine should be sent to him in a bottle on the following day. The patient had a nubile daughter who, as an uncle of mine would put it, "was starting to smell her water", that is, starting to fool around with boys. Anyway, the next day the father gave her the bottle and told her to hurry to the doctor with it and to wait for the result.

On the way she met with some boys and, of course, they fooled and romped around as usual. The bottle fell and broke. To cover up her misdemeanour the girl filled another bottle with her own urine and handed this to the doctor. He went off to test it and, when he came back, he informed her, "Tell your father he's going to have a child."

Writer has heard versions of this tale told in a great many areas.

What's a Po For?

The square of Dundalk was once full of wooden stalls, or "standings", from which salesmen sold all sorts of commodities to the town and country people. Among the traders was a tall figure known as "the delph man" and one day his stall displayed a batch or chamber-pots or poes. A country woman saw the delph and thought to herself, "Just the thing for keeping the butter neat and tidy for sale". She bought one and when next she churned she filled the po with butter, then off she went to Dundalk to sell it. She was surprised when the townspeople objected to her butter, and very puzzled indeed when the authorities came to arrest her. Only then did she discover what the chamber-pot was intended for.

This anecdote was collected in Dromantee, County Armagh, in the 1920s.

A Pound o' Fillet

A country woman set out to buy a chamber-pot from the stall in Dundalk; she was expecting visitors from England and did not want them to have to use a bucket under the bed. The salesman was a tall man with a stentorian voice which required no amplification to be heard. He had chamber-pots for sale but was asking a price which seemed outrageous to the country woman, and they haggled and bargained until the whole town heard them. Finally the trader refused to reduce the price any more and, reluctantly, she bought the po. He offered to wrap it up but she declined angrily, declaring, "I bought it dear and I'm not ashamed of it".

She stalked off with the chamber-pot swinging in her hand, to the embarrassment or, no doubt, sly amusement of many passers-by. In a temper she walked boldly into the fishmonger's and plonked the chamber-pot on the counter. Still hot and bothered she ordered "A pound o' fillet".

"A pound you don't fill it," came the reply.

Told around 1940 in Balnamona, Dromantee parish, County Armagh.

A Time For Everything

An old man from Derrylin, County Fermanagh, was a witness in a court case. In the witness box in Enniskillen he placed the time of the incident concerned in the early morning. He was quizzed as to what kind of time-piece he had or had consulted, and he answered honestly that he had no time-piece at all. Asked then how he had reckoned to time the incident he replied, "It was the second pissing time".

Collected in 1972 in Lisnaskea, County Fermanagh.*

Girls Will Be Boys

A local man was returning in his horse and cart from Monaghan to Scotstown when he came on a teenager – all hair and jeans and sex indistinguishable – who was having trouble with a bicycle; the freewheel was not catching on the cogs so that it could not drive the back wheel. The rider was bouncing the bike on the road hoping that the cogs in the freewheel would free themselves of grease and operate again at least until a repair shop was reached. The man drew abreast of the teenager and saw what the trouble was. "Young fellow," he called, why don't you do what we used to do when your freewheel is missing and you can't get hot water? Piss on it."

"How," asked the teenager.

At that the man clambered out of the cart and told the youngster to hold the bicycle and back wheel parallel to the road; then, slowly revolving the wheel, he urinated on the freewheel. The cogs were released from the grease and the freewheel caught. Thanking the man the cyclist asked where he drank in Scotstown, and then rode on as the man resumed his journey.

When the man reached Scotstown he went into the pub and ordered a pint. When he made to pay for it he was told that two pints of Guinness had already been paid for for him. "By who?" he asked.

"The girl you overtook out the road and got her freewheel to catch," came the answer.

Collected in Scotstown, County Monaghan.*

Equivocal Tales

Children who were allowed to sit around the fireside amid their female elders all heard the equivocal rhymes and riddles, some known in similar versions throughout Ireland, some known only to particular districts. This writer heard them also as a youngster in fireside céilís where the late Mary McDonald, a noted storyteller, was patron. The women took great delight in listening to young boys and girls answer the riddles, while the youngsters could never understand the reason for the hilarity. Each attempted answer reminded the elders of the sexual meaning which only they knew and understood. Of course, in many areas, and particularly where Irish was or had recently been spoken, equivocal English was by no means confined to fireside games.

I put it in dry
I took it out dripping,
And I'd waggle with me arse
Till my face was sweating.

(The churn staff in a kitchen churning.)

My Uncle John has a thing that's long;
My Aunt Mary has a thing that's hairy;
My Uncle John put his thing that's long
Into my Aunt Mary's thing that's hairy.

(Knitting a sock for a man.)

I put my foot between her feet
And she began to jig;
I pulled out my long and hairy thing
And filled her whirlygig.

(A woman at a spinning wheel.)

As I went over the Hill of Comedee
I met an old woman, she was scratching her diddy.
"Diddy," says she, I gave her a clout
And the milk all came spouting out.

(A milk thistle.)

Round about naked;
If your thing doesn't stand
Mine will make it.

(Bonnick bread standing against a bread iron on the hearth after being
baked.)

As I went through thon slippery-slap
I met a beardy lass;
Titty was her tatty
And hairy was her arse.

(A milking goat.)

I laid her down upon her back
And stripped her belly bare;
I pulled out my long and hairy thing
And wrought it through her hair.

(Man clipping a sheep with shears.)

Come wee pun-oodle to big pun-oodle
Put over your pun-oodle to mine;
Put in your pun-oodle
Pull out your pun-oodle
Put over your pun-oodle to mine.

(A woman knitting.)

Two bucks went to foot turf,
Says the buck to the buck
"Would you foot-foot turf?"

(Buck: a male goat.)

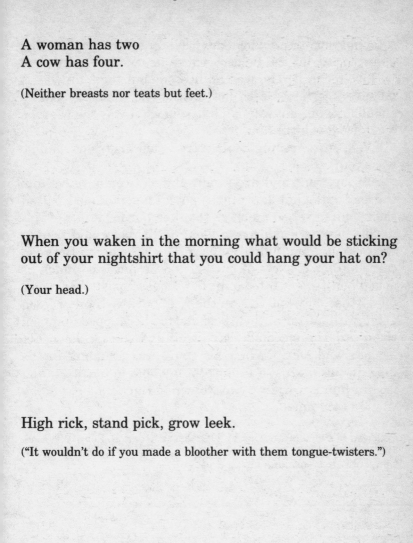

A woman has two
A cow has four.

(Neither breasts nor teats but feet.)

When you waken in the morning what would be sticking
out of your nightshirt that you could hang your hat on?

(Your head.)

High rick, stand pick, grow leek.

("It wouldn't do if you made a bloother with them tongue-twisters.")

Elegant English

There was a woman with very bad English who lived in
Creggan, near Greencastle in County Tyrone. She had a
lint hole or flax dam, where flax was retted, and it came on

a terribly dry year when this well-up neighbour had flax going to loss in the fields because he couldn't get a dam with water in it. The woman had one but the man wasn't on speaking terms with her. In the end someone said he should ask her anyway, and he said what was the use, she wouldn't give it to him.

"Well, sure nothing beats a try," said his friend. "I'll go with you."

So they went and eventually the old woman gave him the lend of the lint dam and he got his flax dammed. But, it seems, he never so much as thanked her for it.

This day he was driving along in his pony and trap to Carrickmore and didn't he pass the old blade on the road carrying her baskets of butter, and he never so much as asked her if she wanted a lift but drove on past. And a wee bit further on what was on the road but two more women going with butter in their baskets and he stopped and took them up. The old blade saw it all and she let down her baskets and said, "When his thing was standing in the field dry as a whistle I lent him my hole to put it in; and look at him now riding two women to Carrickmore and he wouldn't ride me!"

Collected in the 1950s in Glenhull, Greencastle parish, County Tyrone. Termonmagurk and Munterloney, which includes the Glenhull district, were both Irish speaking at the time.

Woeful Desire

A Case of Exposure

A farmer and his teenage servant boy were cleaning out a drain full of mud or *glár*. The hunt was out the same day, with the men clad in jackets and breeches and the women riding side-saddle in skirts. As the hunt came by the two men stood aside to let it pass. But instead of jumping the fence one woman's horse shied, stopped dead, and catapulted the rider over its head and into the drain. The farmer and his servant boy ran to her aid and each caught hold of a leg apiece and pulled her out. When the *glár* had been cleaned from her face and eyes she regained her composure. She unbuttoned a pocket on her riding skirt and took out a purse. "I suppose you're a married man?" she queried the farmer.

"I am, ma'am," he replied.

From the purse she gave him a half-crown. Then to the young fellow she said, "I don't suppose you're married?"

"No, ma'am," he answered.

"Then the sight was good enough for you," she told him, snapping her purse closed.

I heard this tale in the 1930s from a mill worker and a farm labourer in Dromantee parish, County Armagh.

The Horseback Rider with Agility

A Sligo man looking for work came walking into Blacklion; it was a bright and breezy morning, and when he reached the creamery a young woman came by riding a spirited horse. She was a doctor's daughter from Belcoo in County Fermanagh and wore riding skirts. All of a sudden the breeze whipped a newspaper in front of the horse and, startled, she shied and reared. The rider spun and rolled across the animal's back, her heels in the air, and landed on her feet on the road. The horse bolted but the Sligo man had anticipated this action and caught her quickly. When he brought the horse back to the girl she thanked him and handed him a coin. Then she said proudly, "Did you see my agility?"

"I did, ma'am," said he, "though that's not what we call it round Tubbercurry."

As the girl prepared to get back on the horse she enquired, "Did you ever mount a lady?"

"No, ma'am," said he, "though now and again at the fair in Sligo I took an oul' one up the back lanes."

Versions of this tale were heard in Dromantee in the 1930s. I collected this version in Blacklion, County Cavan, in 1976.

No Flasher Was He

This girl went away to America and got a job working for a posh family as a maid. The mistress had a great old fellow who worked as her gardener but he died, so she asked the maid this day, "Would you have a brother at home in Ireland that would come over? He'd have a great time here in the garden."

"I have a brother at home," said the girl.

"Well tell him to come over," said the mistress. "If he'd be better off at home let him stop there, but he'd have a great time here."

So she wrote to the brother; he came over some time later and when he arrived at the house Mary was in the kitchen cleaning lobsters for the dinner. He was fierce curious about the lobsters – he had never seen one before – so he picked one up to look at it. Next thing a step came up and, frightened of being caught maybe doing something wrong, he stuck it down the front of his trousers.

The mistress came in and gave him a great welcome. Then she said, "Now that Mary is getting the dinner, we'll have a walk in the garden to pass the time."

They went through the garden and round the garden, and all the time he was grabbing at the crotch of his trousers for the lad was beginning to nip him. The brother was trying to keep as quiet as he could, you know, not to let the lady see him, but the lobster was moving down, you see, and nipping him. They went on, round and round the garden, with the mistress pointing out the different flowers to him.

"Bejasus, ma'am," he burst out finally, "take your time till I get the lad out!"

The lady made for the house as quick as she could. "This is a desperate character you brought over," she said to Mary. "I couldn't have that fellow about the house at all!"

The mistress left and shortly afterwards Mary's brother came back in. "What in the wide world," said Mary, "happened to you. The mistress is all frightened; 'twas an awful thing to say."

"It was that ould damn thing that I put in and I hadn't time to ask you what it was. What could I do? I had to stop to take the bugger out."

Mary went and explained the whole story to the mistress, and after that the brother worked in the garden for years and never took out the lad any more.

Collected in Blacklion, County Cavan, in 1972.

It's All the Same

A man believed that his wife was not giving him the sexual satisfaction he was entitled to or led to expect, so he started to go "on the country", that is, to seek sexual intercourse with whatever girls or married women consented to his approaches. But after such encounters he was heard to grumble, "It's all the same, all the same".

One husband, hearing of his escapades and suspicious of the man's visits to his wife, lay in wait for him. When the fellow came out of the house he was muttering to himself, "It's all the same. It's all the same".

"What's all the same?" the husband shot out at him.

"The price these women are asking for their geese and turkeys," replied your man.

Collected in Clarnagh, near Crossmaglen, County Armagh, and in Dromantee also in the 1930s.

Lowering the Rent

Meredith Champré, or Chamber-lye as he was called locally, was a landlord in Dromantee in the 1840s. He exacted high rents off his tenants, many of whom he evicted so as to turn their small farms into large fields for pasture and crop. In 1852 an assassination attempt was made on Champré in which he lost an eye, and a local Dromantee man, Francis Barry, was hanged in Armagh for his complicity in the plot. Following this attack there were further mass evictions in which Catholic tenants were replaced by Protestants, but due to pressure brought on by government inquiries Champré later relented and gave a reduction in rent to tenants with families, the reduction being in ratio to the size of the family.

Walking along the road one day he met the wife of one of his tenants who was also a worker on the estate. The man had for some days failed to turn up for work, so Champré asked the woman the reason for her husband's absence.

"Master Champré," she informed him, "he's at home in bed with a pain in his back from trying to lower the rent."

Temptress

A boy and girl in their late teens had been working together in the bog and were carrying the turf home in wicker-woven back creels. On the way back to the house they rested at a turf bank in a secluded spot and, playfully, the boy tried to grab at the girl and get in hoults with her.

She ran, crying out, "Don't do that again. You frighten the life out of me!"

The boy desisted and they heaved their creels of turf on their shoulders again and went on. Before reaching the path to the house they had to rest once more in a wee hollow, but this time the boy was quiet and still. Suddenly the girl said, "You know, you should frighten me again."

Collected in Blacklion, County Cavan, in 1980.

In an Irish Dance Hall

A group of young fellows came in after the pub to the Irish dance hall in Berkinhead in England. One of the group was a small, wiry looking type, with noticeably big ears which stuck out from his head. He noticed a girl nearby with very prominent breasts; though he didn't know it, she was from Crossmaglen where people are noted for their sharp wits and one doesn't have to "look for an answer". The big-eared fellow strolled up to the girl, prodded her on her breasts, and asked cheekily, "What's them?"

"Them," she replied smartly, "is wee bags of oats I carry for coaxing asses like you." The lad's companions laughed. Then the girl added, "Hi, boy. Pin back those ears or they'll batter your eyes out in the wind," and she moved away.

The Cold Crayther

Two old people made a match and got married. There was no big spread, no honeymoon or anything; they just went to the chapel and got married, came back home and done the necessary work about the house, and that night they went to bed. And of course there was nothing doing at all, and when they were in bed for an hour the old lady said, "John, I'm perished with the cold".

"God, you must be a cold crayther," said John, and he went to the kitchen, boiled the kettle and filled a hot-water bottle, and he brought it up and fired it into the bed to her. "Now," he said, "maybe that'll keep you warm."

That was all right anyway, but in an hour's time she started elbowing him, "I'm cold again, John".

He went down to the kitchen and this time he brought up every old coat he could find in the house and he fired them in on top of her. "Maybe that'll keep you warm," he said. "Now, can't you let me have a bit of sleep?"

But in another hour's time she started nudging him again. "John, I'm perished with the cold again. And do you know," she went on, "if me poor old mother was here she'd put her two arms around me and she'd hug me and she'd keep me as warm as toast-cake."

"Don't think," said John, "that I'm going to get up in the middle of the night to get your ould mother to keep you warm. Not one bit of fear of me."

Collected in Blacklion, County Cavan, in 1978.*

A Rousing Bridal Night

A newly married couple retired after the wedding celebrations to the room specially prepared for them, unaware that the tick had been secretly set with sprouts of whin bushes by pranksters. As they settled down the whin thorns pierced the tick and jabbed the new bride in the buttocks. She began to cry out because as she moved she was pricked by still more thorns.

The husband's father was still sitting in the kitchen and hearing the cries he called out chastisingly to his son, "Damn your soul, can't you take her easy".

Newly-weds getting into bed on the first night often found that companions had played pranks on them, such as knotting the sheets or putting thorns in the bed. I took down versions of the latter prank from storytellers.

The Thinker

A man found employment on a farm as a servant boy and one day was put whitewashing the inside of a barn. One of the girls of the family came out to see the stranger out of curiosity, just as he took a break from his work so as to urinate. Pointing to his penis the girl asked, "What's that?"

"That," he replied, "is a thinker."

She asked him what it was thinking about and he said, "He says there's a bum-bees' nest in the bottom of your belly and unless he goes in to rob it the bees will sting you to death."

He copulated with the girl quickly and then, all agog with excitement, she ran into the house to tell her mother and sister what had happened. They chastised her for being so credulous, but the girl insisted it was all true and to prove it lifted up her clothes.

"If you don't believe me," she exclaimed, "look at the honey running down my legs."

I heard this tale and variants of it around Dromantee parish in the 1920s, and collected a version from County Cavan in the 1970s.*

Arse About Turn

"I wouldn't use arse for a thousand acres," said the Ulster woman, an expression commonly heard when a story with arse was involved. Or when, for example, seating was restricted and a woman made room for another person on a stool or form, she said, "Fire your arse down on that". I heard another usage from the late Mickey Finnegan. He had loaned some farm implement to a neighbour who had not returned it, to which Mickey said: "When you lend your arse you may shite through your teeth".

Arsing About

Brigid had emigrated from the countryside to New York where she got a position as a servant girl in a big house in the suburbs. She liked her mistress and the mistress, in turn, was charmed by Brigid. In time Brigid sent the fare home to her brother; she also sent directions on how to find the big house she worked in because emigrants in those days could be held for unpredictable lengths of time by the emigration authorities at Ellis Island. She also warned her brother to watch his country tongue before her mistress and master who were very polite in their manners. The brother was not unduly profane or foul-mouthed any more than his neighbours, though people used "hoor" and "bastard" as superlatives in the Elizabethan fashion and thought nothing of it.

When the brother arrived at the house Brigid was not at home. Her mistress explained that she had sent Brigid on a message and that she would be back soon; the mistress invited him in meanwhile for coffee and cookies. He thanked her but declined the invitation saying, "I'll just arse about till our one comes back".

I first heard this tale in Dromantee, County Armagh, in the 1920s.

"You Don't Leave Your Card Here, Sir!"

The girl had lately arrived in the USA and her country style of talk and diction was still too free. One day when cleaning a room she swore and her mistress, hearing what she had said, reprimanded her. The mistress asked her why she had spoken so roughly, and the servant girl replied: "Sure the cat shit under the bed, ma'am!"

The mistress was most disturbed. She told the girl that she must never use that word: in future in such a contingency she was to say that "the cat left his card under the bed".

A few days later a visitor called when the family was out. The servant girl told the man that the family was out of town.

"Then I'll just go into the drawing room and leave my card," he said.

"By God you will not then," replied the girl smartly. "You don't leave your card here, sir!"

Another anecdote concerning emigrant serving girls from Dromantee, County Armagh.

The Hunker Slider

Biddy was a character in the town of Newry. She was addicted to a cheap wine known as "Red Biddy" and as a result was often brought before the local magistrate for being drunk and disorderly. The magistrate knew all the characters who frequented his court and often bantered with those who were without fear of him and, indeed, capable of giving him a tart reply. The magistrate enjoyed these sessions as he was a wit himself.

Once, after she had been absent from any court proceedings for an unusually long time, Biddy was brought before the magistrate's bench. When the policeman had put his case and proved that Biddy had been involved in a disturbance the magistrate said to her, "Biddy, I missed you. Where were you this long time?"

"I was in heaven," Biddy replied.

"In heaven? And how did you get back to earth?"

"I grazed me arse and slid down a rainbow," said Biddy sarcastically.

"In that case, Biddy," said the magistrate, "for your hunker sliding I'll give you a month in Armagh."

Told to me in the 1930s in Dromantee, County Armagh.

Eve and the Apple

A girl from Munterloney had gone as a servant to the house of a parson in Cookstown in County Tyrone. A staunch Roman Catholic, she had been warned before accepting employment that her master was a "black Protestant".

It was the era when Roman Catholics were forbidden to eat meat on Fridays, and when Friday came the girl was offered meat which she refused to eat. The parson wanted to know why she refused such a sustaining meal: she replied that it would be a mortal sin for her to eat it.

"Do you not know that the Good Book sayeth that whatever entereth the mouth doth not defile the soul?" said the parson.

"Was it with her arse that Eve ate the apple so?" the girl replied.

Collected in the early 1950s in Carnanrancy, Greencastle parish, County Tyrone.

An Inja Rubber Horse

For the first time ever a circus had come to a remote town in the west of Ireland. During the night the circus elephant escaped and a clown was sent to search the countryside for the animal, but no one he met knew what an elephant was or looked like. The clown walked on. At length he met a man and asked him, "Have you seen an elephant hereabouts?"

"What's an elephant?" replied the man.

The clown walked on, saying to himself, "No use asking him". He met a second man some miles further on and asked, "Have you seen an elephant on your travels?"

"A what?" said the second man.

The clown walked some miles further and met a third man. He asked, "Have you seen an elephant on your road?"

"What's an elephant?" said the third man, and again the clown walked on.

But the other man called out and said to the clown: "I don't know what an elephant is, but there's a bloody big Inja rubber horse back in Magee's field, and he's pulling the turnips with his tail and sticking them up his arse!"

I heard many versions of this tale, the latest being in 1970 in the Glangevlin district of County Cavan. It was first told to me in the 1920s by my father, the late Michael Murphy of Dromantee, County Armagh.*

The Old-Age Pensioner

An old woman set out from the hills to draw her first old age pension in Blacklion. The pension had just been introduced and she was very excited at getting "five shillings for nothing", though she did not feel sure that it would be paid. Arriving at the post office, with time to spare, she had a look around the village. She caught a reflection of herself in a mirror in a shop window: she was very flushed and not at all aged looking. In fact, she thought to herself, she looked too good to claim any pension. But then, as she said, "I went back out of Blacklion up that old road from the village and sat on me bare arse on a big stone till I'd cool down. And then I went back for my pension."

Collected in Wheathill, County Fermanagh, about 1980.

A Puzzled Servant Boy

Johnny was a small man with a very easy-going temperament. He was a casual farm labourer but relied for his main source of income on the maintenance of a stretch of road running from the border of Armagh and Louth towards the town of Dundalk. In the parlance of the time he "took a stretch of road", that is, took a contract from the county council to maintain the surface of the road, trim the sheughs or grass margins, and keep the water-passages cut in the roadside ditch clear so as to allow surface flood water to escape to a soakage in the contiguous fields.

It was in May when the hawthorn hedges were in full leaf that Johnny, with his long-tailed shovel, was clearing such an escape into a large, hilly field belonging to a landowner named Bradford who kept a few hired servant boys. One of the lads working in the field came down towards the passageway. Johnny realised that because of the leafy hedges the young fellow had not seen him, or indeed the blade of his shovel positioned in the passageway. The young fellow "loosed a button" and squatted over the passageway to defecate, and Johnny, impishly, pushed his shovel forward until the blade was directly beneath the boy's backside. Once the lad had relieved himself and was standing erect to button up, Johnny quietly withdrew his shovel back through the opening in the ditch.

The servant boy, about to go back to his work, turned and looked, then stared, looked and stared again. Then he declared, "I coulda swore I dunged there!"

This was told to me in Tievecrom in Dromantee parish, County Armagh.

Both the Same Material

Paddy got a job as coachman to a vicar in a fairly remote part of Yorkshire. He was a Roman Catholic, of course. There was only one Roman Catholic church in the entire area and this was made with galvanised iron, like scores of cattle sheds along the way. Out driving the vicar and his wife one day Paddy ignored all the sheds, but when approaching and passing the chapel he reverently raised his hat. Eventually the vicar said to him, "Paddy, I notice you only raise your hat to one building and not the others. Why is that?"

"There's a difference, your reverence," said Paddy.

"I see no difference," replied the vicar, "they're all made of the one material."

Paddy pulled up and turned to the vicar. "Reverend sir," he asked, "do you kiss your wife?"

"Of course I kiss my wife," said the vicar.

"Do you ever kiss her arse?"

"Certainly not," the vicar retorted crossly.

"Why not?" persisted Paddy.

"Ah, there's a difference, Paddy."

"I see no difference, reverend sir. They're both made of the one material."

Collected in Dromantee, County Armagh, in the 1930s.

"You Do It There!"

Two Irishmen made a bet: one bet that he could trick a Jewish tailor into giving him a new suit; the other bet he could not. Neither of the pair had the price of a suit to begin with.

The first Irishman went into the Jewman's shop, examined the toilet and saw it had a window big enough to let him out. He went up to the Jewman and said that he was going to be married the next day and wanted a new suit: "a new rig-out from top to toe". The Jewman was delighted with such a customer, took some measurements and showed his ready-made wares. The Irishman selected one and then asked if he could fit it on. This done he also selected a new shirt and tie and new shoes to go with it.

Suddenly the Irishman was seized with a severe pain in his guts. He asked the Jewman where was the toilet and when it was pointed out he went in and closed the door, leaving his old clothes on the floor. Then, clad in the new suit, he made his escape through the toilet window. He showed the new rig-out to the other Irishman and won his bet.

The second Irishman was peeved and bet that the next day he, too, would get a similar rig-out from the Jewman. The other said that he would not, and a second bet was made. So the next day the other Irishman went into the Jewman's shop and said he was leaving home and wanted a new rig-out from top to toe. As before the Jewman obliged, and the Irishman stood in his new clothes. Then he took a severe stomach pain and asked the Jewman where the toilet was.

The Jewman seized an old newspaper and spread it in the corner of the shop. "You don't leave me sight," he said, indicating the spread-out newspaper. "You do it there!"

Collected in Blacklion, County Cavan.

The Dutch Doctor

There was a doctor, supposed to be a Dutchman, and it was said he could cure anything; he would charge one pound for each cure, but if his treatment failed to effect a cure he would pay the patient the sum of five pounds.

Some local young men said the doctor was a quack and an imposter, and they set out to prove it and expose him. So they whipped up in those impecunious times and among them made up the doctor's fee of one pound. One young man was set to put on an act and pretend he had three ailments: a bad appetite, a bad memory, and a bad habit of telling lies. So he went and told his three complaints to the doctor. The doctor went into the room and came out with this pill, and he told the young man to put it in his mouth and swallow it. So he did.

"How do you feel now?" the doctor asked.

"Pure shite," said the other.

"Well," said the doctor, "you told the truth for once in your life; and anyone that can ate shite has no bad appetite. And as long as you live you'll remember you ate shite."

I collected but two versions of this tale in the Ulster counties: one in the early 1950s in Layde, Cushendall, County Antrim; the second in 1979 in Blacklion, County Cavan, where the storyteller had heard the anecdote in his native parish of Cleenish, County Fermanagh, which lies northwards across Lough MacNean.

The County Antrim tale has but a single motif involving this matter of taste and is told as being true. This version concerns a local herbalist: a young man claims he is an imposter and sets out to prove it to a friend. In the Cavan version, given here, there are three motifs.*

The Lad

There was an old custom used in some areas to allay the fears a new bride might have at the approach of her husband: when the couple went to bed together, a young boy of ten or eleven years was put into the bridal bed along with them. The people believed that the presence of the boy chastened the man in his sexual advances and at the same time gave the woman confidence. At all events, the custom acknowledged that the man's penis had to be curbed – and why wouldn't it? Even in petticoats boys knew that they were special. They wore the same dress as girls not because they were like them, but to deceive the fairies who would use only *male* children to replenish the blood of their tribe. The penis conferred prestige. Just as well, then, not to take it too seriously.

The Spare Penis

It was the time of the Second World War, the time of the smuggling, and the customs men at Belcoo would take everything off you coming over the border from Blacklion. Belcoo is a village in County Fermanagh in Northern Ireland and less than a mile from the village of Blacklion in the Republic. This man from Glenfarne, County Leitrim, got drunk in Blacklion and was having a last drink in Greene's public house before going home on the train from Belcoo. Greene's was also a butcher's, and when he wanted some beef, for a cod they made up a sort of parcel for him of an old cow's elder [udder] and gave it to him for beef.

In order to escape the customs man the old men wore loose trousers so they could stick a parcel down in front, which is what this man did. When he arrived at Belcoo for the train he had to relieve himself but he didn't button up the fly of his trousers right afterwards, and whatever way the Greenes tied the parcel it was tied to scatter. When he got into the train the parcel set off and one of the tits of the cow's elder slipped out through his fly. At the sight of this two women in the carriage started to scream.

The man looked down and saw what had happened; he put his hand in his pocket and took out a clasp knife, and when he opened the knife the two women screamed worse than ever for him not to do it. Holding the tit with one hand he said to it, "You've shamed and disgraced me, but you'll never do it again".

He cut off the tit and threw it out the window, and the women screamed even more. "Quit your screaming," he said to them, "I have spare ones here."

Collected in Moneygashel, Blacklion, County Cavan.*

No Compo for Peter

Old Pete was a comical wag. He got a job working on the railway and when they were shovelling clay or something he got into the wagon to flatten it out, but the train moved a bit and he fell off. He got hurted a bit. He didn't work for weeks after but he got all right and, anyway, he was up for compensation. He knew he'd have to go before a medical board in Enniskillen; the railway company had a doctor looking after their own interests who would do a check-up. His name was Kidd.

Well, Peter went down the road on two sticks. He was bad, very bad, in fact he was never as lame in his life. He went into Enniskillen on the train but when he came back that evening he wasn't near as lame as setting out. A lock of us pitching buttons [playing pitch and toss] asked him how he had got on with Kidd.

"Bad luck to him," said Peter, "it's not Kidd he should be called but wolf!"

He would give us no more information but we found it out after. When Peter went in the doctor ordered him to strip and to hurry up about it. "Ah, doctor," said Peter, "if you were as bad as me you wouldn't be asking me to hurry."

"Come on, you'll keep me all night," said Kidd, and whatever kind of pluck or nip he give Peter he had him going up the wall like a cat: no cat could climb the wall quicker to get away from him!

So that finished Peter's compensation.

Collected in Blacklion, County Cavan, in 1978.*

Penis in a Trap

There was a Yankee, a returned Irish-American, and his
wife, a "pure" American who had strong biblical feelings
about life and its vicissitudes. Each evening, accompanied
by his wife and their little dog, he would walk at dusk to
the Black Bridge near Glenfarne, a hamlet in County
Leitrim. He'd go to the bridge to piss into the stream.
Some local young men noticed this customary evening
visit of the Yankee and set rat traps on the wall of the
bridge at the spot where he used stand. Next evening the
Yankee came along and rested his lad on the bridge to
piss, and he sprang one of the traps. He yelled and
screamed, but his wife shouted at him to have patience,
like Job.

"Job never had his balls caught in a rat trap!" cried the
Yankee.

I recorded versions of this story from narrators in the parish of
Killinagh, County Cavan, and in Wheathill, County Fermanagh. This
version was collected in 1979 in Killykeegan, County Fermanagh, and
had previously been heard in Geevagh in County Sligo, an area noted
for storytelling.*

Brigid Saw Blood

Brigid had emigrated to the USA and found a job with
wealthy Jews in New York as a nurse-maid. One of her
main tasks was to take the children to the park and, after
another infant had been born to the family, Brigid was in
due course told to take it out for air in the perambulator. It

76

was a fine day but with a spirited breeze, and on the way the breeze lifted the coverlet on the pram and lifted the infant's dress too, exposing its penis. Brigid saw a welter of blood on the boy's genitals and fled in panic back to her employer's house, crying out that they fetch a doctor immediately. When she described what she had seen her mistress tried to calm her. "Don't worry, Brigid," she said, "that's just part of our Jewish religion. It's what we call circumcision."

"Oh, God be good to old Ireland," cried Brigid, "they wouldn't cut the black off your nail if it grew to be the length of a shovel shaft!"

Heard in Dromantee, County Armagh, in the 1920s.

The Quickest Growth

A father wanted to test his daughters, so he set them this question: "What has the quickest growth?" The eldest girl thought it might be the hawthorn sprout, so he put the question to the second girl. "The briar has the quickest growth," she answered him.

He turned to the third and youngest daughter and said, "Tell me, what has the quickest growth?"

"A man's tool," the girl replied.

Heard in Dromantee, County Armagh, in the 1930s.

In Petticoats or Not

A boy who lived with his grandmother was summonsed in a paternity suit by the parents of a young deaf and dumb girl. The grandmother accompanied him to court on the day of the hearing and after the charge had been read out she stood her grandson up on a bench. It was the time when boys still wore petticoats until an advanced age, and the grandmother lifted high his petticoats and, pointing to his genitals, she asked, "How could such a young lad be accused of being the parent of that girl's child?"

When the speech had been translated to her in sign language the mute girl sprang to her feet. With one hand she caught her other forearm, closed her fist and shook it at the boy's penis.

Collected in Dromantee, County Armagh.*

A Bridal Night Dread

This lassie got married and she was worried because she had only a thin brush of [pubic] hair. So she got, or was told to get, a rabbit skin for the first night, and she wore it someway on her private parts. The man banged and banged away the whole night but the next night she didn't have the rabbit skin on at all, and he said to her, "How is it that last night it was all hair and no hole, and the night it's all hole and no hair?"

Collected in Wheathill, County Fermanagh, in 1979.*

Black Pudding

One time an aged, miserly man from Killinagh went into an eating house in Enniskillen and asked to be served with the cheapest dinner the woman of the house had available. The woman told him that it would cost two pence, and he put the coins on the table. She went into the kitchen and returned with a single black pudding which she served him on a plate. At this the miser grabbed back his tuppence, jumped to his feet and stormed out, declaring, "Cheap or not, I'm not going to eat any jack-ass's tool!"

Collected in Killinagh parish, Blacklion, County Cavan.

Love is a Wondrous Thing

In parts of County Cavan illicit sexual encounters were called "thieving", just as people talked of a trespassing cow as "thieving". This term applied especially to a married woman involved with a man other than her husband. "There was no word of this love when I was a young fellow," a County Armagh parish priest thundered from his pulpit, but though he denounced sexual sin, he might have thought of the practice of matchmaking which was never condemned from pulpit or in pastoral, as it should have been. While it worked well for many, matchmaking could also be crude and insensitive. In one such match, which was eventually settled to the satisfaction of both sets of parents, neither the boy nor girl was present. The girl was asleep and knew nothing of what was going on until her mother called her, "Put your smart way about you and put on your best things".

"Why, ma, what's up?" asked the girl.

"You're going to be married, that's what's up."

"To who, ma?"

"Never you mind who," her mother responded, "it's none of your business."

Women were of course more sexually constrained than men and indeed the tradition of applying chastity belts to women was still known and mentioned, especially in County Antrim. A girl sent on a message to another part of the locality, and having to pass the house of a known lecher on the way, would have a chastity belt "stitched and double stitched" onto her body to protect her vagina. There was a strong cultural emphasis on virginity and the maidenhead. I remember that when young boys and girls were playing together or indulging in horse-play, if a girl was accidently scratched or knocked and blood was drawn the girl cried, "Now you've gone and drawn me blood. Now you'll have to marry me".

Girls were advised not to expect much from men; any having a "scud of a court" with a man who told her he loved her was said afterwards to be "pure daft in the head". Love did hold an attraction though. The late Barney Shortt of Carricksticken, Dromantee, had a definition of his own. "I'd say this love must be like the drink," he would advise. "From what I hear you no sooner have a sup than you want to go back for more."

I'm for America

A man and his wife lived on a "tidy wee farm" with their family. They had just one daughter and eventually a match was made for her with a hired man who had come to the district. The marriage was set, and on the night before the wedding the hired man stayed with the girl's family. There was a half-loft over the kitchen and the two men, the hired man and his future father-in-law, decided to sleep there while the daughter would spend the night with her mother. They climbed up to the loft and went to bed, talked together for a while and then fell silent.

Meanwhile the girl and her mother remained below in the kitchen sitting beside the fire and discussing the wedding. When the men grew silent the two women thought they had gone to sleep, and in a little while the girl said quietly to her mother, "I didn't mention thon to him, ma, that I had a child".

"What?" hissed the fellow on the loft, "had she a child to someone?"

"She had," her father confirmed.

"Then," said the man, getting out of bed and making towards the gable window, "I'm for America."

Down in the kitchen the mother was advising her daughter. "And why should you mention it to him?" she told her. "He'll never find out now. Sure I had one before I married your father and he never knew."

"Wait!" shouted the father as the fellow scrambled through the window. "I'm for America too!"

Collected in the 1950s from a storyteller from Forkhill, County Armagh.

Skinning Another One

Old L – was a bit of a romancer: he fancied every lady he seen travelling, women or tramp women or any damn thing; he couldn't let a scarecrow with a skirt pass. He met this big one anyway and he brought her to one of his fields, behind where the graveyard is now, and they lay down behind the ditch. Just at the same time this other fellow, a very short-sighted fellow, was coming down the road. He had occasion to cross the ditch at the same place; he crossed the ditch and got down on his hunkers and just then he seen L –, he knew him by his coat. L – had lost a lot of cattle that year from some disease, a lot of them took something and died, and when this man seen the white legs and every damn thing under the coat he thought L – must be skinning another dead beast. And he pipes up, "Ah, me poor fellow, are you skinning another one?"

Collected in Blacklion, County Cavan.

Going Round the Lough

A girl who had an illegitimate child was compelled to make public penance for her sin, which in this instance consisted of crawling on her knees around the shores of a small lough in County Down. As she crept along her knees undavoidably tugged on the hem of her skirt, pulling it down. There was a man also doing a round of the lough on his knees to make public penance for committing the sin of fornication elsewhere.

Workers in a nearby field looked at them as they did the round and one man saw that the girl was having difficulty with her skirt. He shouted to the man to lift her skirt for her.

"No bloody fear," the man replied, "It's that has me on my knees!"

I heard this tale in the 1960s in Lurgancanty, County Down. I have heard a version broadcast on radio by a young priest who took the folktale for fact and used the story to underline the need for forgiveness and charity.

Canonical Penance and Public Satisfaction

I knew an old woman who was ten years of age at the start of the Famine and she minded [remembered] it all. She minded a woman in Glenfarne in County Leitrim, a young woman who'd had an illegitimate baby, and that was a crime. Oh, if you spoke to her on the road you were a criminal too; everybody was encouraged to treat them as outcasts and not to let them into their house. Now I don't know whether it was right or not, but the penance when the baby was delivered and all was that the mother had to come to Mass on Sunday with a white sheet on her, and she had to stand in the aisle while Mass was going on. When the congregation stood up at the Gospel she had to kneel down, and when the Gospel was over she had to stand up again.

Well, this old woman – she married into our place to a man called McEniff – remembered, "I never got such a scare in my life. I was kneeling at the end of the seat up at the very altar," she said, "and I had to go to the rails. When I went to get communion all of a sudden this lassie with the white sheet on her come and stood at the end of the seat. God, I thought it was something unearthly!"

"But there was some priest," old Anne McEniff said, "a younger type of priest from the old crowd, and he turned around to preach after the last gospel.

"'I see a female the day in white doing Canonical penance,' he said. 'I'm not the cause of that and I'll guarantee,' he goes on, 'that it'll be the last time the name of St Mary's will be desecrated here by any female coming in white. Go into your seat, go into a seat, please, and sit down,' he told the woman."

And that was the last woman ever done Canonical penance in Glenfarne chapel.

I collected this story in Blacklion, County Cavan, and, unusually, the storyteller provided the title.

Now You've Gone and Drawn Me Blood

A young girl who was very much constrained by her father at last insisted that she was entitled to go to the local town on a "set day", that is, a Church holiday. The father finally relented but before allowing her to go he said she would have to let him tie a cloth protection between her legs, and he "tied some sort of drawers" on her. In town the girl met some boy; there was some sexual play between them and the girl began to bleed. To stem the blood she tore the drawers into rags and stuffed them into her vagina, but when she returned home her father examined her.

"I sent you out with a brand new maidenhead," he exclaimed, "and you come home to me with one rid to rags!"

I heard this tale in many parts of Ulster where I collected folklore.*

Sign Here

The doctor told a woman that she was not to conceive again or she would be "signing her own death warrant" and advised her to sleep apart from her husband. She moved to a separate room until one night she appeared at her husband's bed and said, "I've come to sign my death warrant".

"Right," said the husband, "I have the pen in me hand."

Heard in Blacklion, County Cavan, about 1979.

The Gamey Wife

A man visited a boon companion who had recently married. That night a storm prevented the visitor from leaving their house so he was put up for the night in the same bed as the man and his wife. The woman slept next to the wall while the husband positioned himself between his wife and his companion. The next morning, when the storm had passed, the visitor made to leave. As he did so he commented to his friend, "That's a gamey wife you have".

"Why so?" the husband asked.

"She had a grip of my lad all night."

"She had not," said the husband. "That was me."

Collected in Dromantee, County Armagh.*

You Can Trust No Woman

These two men were working together in the bog, chatting and talking, and one of the men, a widow man, said to the other, "Do you know, you can trust no woman".

"How is that?" said the other.

"Well," said the widower, "I'll prove it to you. Let you by the way drop dead. I'll go down to your wife and say that you're after taking a turn and that you died. You think that you have a great woman, that she wouldn't let you down, so we'll just test her."

The husband agreed to try it, so the widower went down to his wife. "Your husband is after dropping dead in the bog," he told her. The wife was stricken so the widower said he would take care of the arrangements for the wake. That night the neighbours all came to say how sorry they were to hear of her husband's death but later the widower said to the wife, "Look at this now. Your husband is dead and I'm living, and I'm a widow man. What about me and you hitting it off? Sure your husband is gone." The wife agreed to his suggestion, but the man continued, "I have just one wee fault, and just to be fair I'll tell you. I do wet the bed."

"Sure that's nothing," answered the wife. "There's a villain lying there and he rotted more sheets than I could keep on him."

Her husband's "corpse" suddenly leapt to life. "You're a bloody liar! I rotted no sheets on you!"

Collected in Blacklion, County Cavan, in 1972. I have taken down other versions also, and indeed John M. Synge based his famous play *The Shadow of the Glen* on a version of this tale he heard in Wicklow or the West.

She Didn't Know What She Was Missing

There was a young married woman who had been a servant for many years to an aged spinster, and continued in the spinster's service after she got married. The spinster believed that she was soon to die but was reconciled to her fate. She had been satisfied with her life, she told the servant, and had enjoyed everything a woman could experience. The servant, however, reminded her that she had never married and did not know what it was to lie with a man; that she had missed the delights of the marriage bed. The spinster agreed that this was so.

In a chest in her bedroom the spinster kept a hoard of gold sovereigns which, as she had reminded her servant time and time again, she had saved to pay for her wake and burial. However, having thought about what the servant had said, in the end she asked her if she would agree to an arrangement: would she ask her husband to spend a night with her so she would see what she had missed in the marriage bed? As recompense the husband could take half the sovereigns.

The servant's husband agreed to the offer and spent a night with the spinster, and in the morning he left with half of the hoard as promised. When his wife, the servant, arrived for work the spinster was still in bed. The servant asked her how she felt, and how she felt about the night spent with a man.

"If he comes up the night again," the old spinster replied, "he can take the other half of the gold sovereigns, and let the bloody parish bury me!"

I overheard this tale being told by a group of three elderly people in a bar in Newry, County Down, around 1976. All were natives of an area close to Forkhill in County Armagh.

Priest and Parson

In predominantly Roman Catholic districts of Ulster – indeed, of all of Ireland – and even where the population is mixed the parson is almost invariably the butt of the joke, the folk anecdote and the folk-tale proper. One can speculate on the reasons for this, but I have found no comparable corpus of folk tradition in which the priest is the victim of the tale. There are a few tales in which the Protestant clergyman tells a tale against himself and draws in his Catholic counterpart who is very often a good friend also, but though I enquired from storytellers who were friends of mine, men of the Church of Ireland and Presbyterian faiths, they had never heard any mention and had certainly not told any tales which lampooned priests. Yet they had stories in which the clergymen of their own faiths were the butt of the tales, and these they told with gusto.

A Sharp Wit

The Church of Ireland rector in Cushendall, Canon Sharp, was a good friend of his Roman Catholic counterpart, Canon O'Rawe, and both were noted wits. Canon Sharp used visit Dan Hyndman, a bachelor and storyteller, as often as he could and on one such visit he told Dan of a dream which Canon O'Rawe had had. Canon O'Rawe had dreamt that he and Canon Sharp had been travelling together but had been killed suddenly in a railway accident. They had gone to heaven and Canon Sharp had reached the gates before Canon O'Rawe. An angel at the gate had handed him a thick stick of chalk, pointed to a spiral staircase ascending to heaven proper, and instructed the canon to write the sins of his life singly on each step as he ascended. Canon O'Rawe had arrived later and had also been given a stick of chalk. Then, O'Rawe recounted, "I wasn't quarter of the way up when I met Canon Sharp coming down for more chalk".

Collected in Cusskib, County Antrim, in the 1950s.

The Parson's Nose and Tail

There was a young and handsome wife in an early stage of pregnancy. She was a Protestant and when the parson called to see her he commented on her condition. Then he informed her that he had bad news for her: the child, he said, would be born without a nose. However, he could remedy this deformity by having intercourse with the woman and so put a nose on the child. The woman agreed and they copulated.

When her husband returned from work that evening the woman told him of the parson's visit and what had occurred. The husband made no reply, but left the house. The parson had sheep grazing on the glebe lands and the husband went there and started to cut the tails off the sheep. The parson saw him and rushed to rebuke him for maiming the sheep. The husband dismissed the parson's outrage sharply. "When you can put noses on children," he told him, "you can surely put tails on sheep."

Collected in Dromantee, County Armagh, in the 1930s.*

The Cattle Dealer and the Parson

In the era before the cattle lorry arrived on the roads, cattle dealers throughout Ireland walked from fair to fair, buying stock at one market in the hope of selling at a profit at another. In the summer they slept at night along the roads with their cattle and in winter they were often at the mercy of the weather.

A cattle dealer who found himself benighted one wild and wet winter's night was keeping a special look-out for signs of a house where he might seek shelter until morning. At last he spied a light and made his way to it. The house proved to be the residence of an old-time parson who made the cattle dealer welcome and offered him food. Then the parson told the dealer that he would give him shelter for the night but, as it was a small manse in a desolate countryside, the parsonage had only one bed. However, the cattle dealer, if he wished, was welcome to share it with the parson. The cattle dealer didn't mind one bit.

They went to bed but before settling down the parson said, "Don't mind if you hear me talking in my sleep. I'm told I preach from my sermons."

The cattle dealer replied that indeed he had the same trouble himself at times, and the parson should not be disturbed or upset if he should start to make fair-day bargains and gesticulate with his hands in his sleep.

They fell asleep but a little while later the parson got to his feet and in his sleep intoned, "And what did Abraham say?"

At this the cattle dealer sprang up in his sleep, slapped the parson on the arse and cried, "I'll split the difference with you!"

The actions woke them both. They apologised to one another and went back to sleep once more. But in a short while the parson was again on his feet declaiming, "And what did Paul say?"

The cattle dealer rose to his feet and, still asleep, caught the parson by the penis. "Get into the wagon," he bellowed, "or I'll screw the tail out of you!"

Collected in Dromantee, County Armagh.

The Preaching Contest

When the old parson retired his ministry was to be taken over by a freshly ordained young man. The two clerics met to discuss contemporary religious practices and the values of old and new approaches to the preaching of the sermon. The young parson upheld the current approach, but the older man disputed this contention and claimed that he could preach a sermon that would have one part of the congregation in fear, weeping and dread while at the same time the other part would be laughing. The young parson challenged his senior to carry off such a feat and they set the following Sunday as the date for the contest.

The next Sunday the old minister went up to the pulpit to preach. He took as his text the theme that out of hell there was no redemption, and he dwelt long and vividly on the torture of the damned souls condemned to remain forever in the same hell. But at a high point of emotion in his sermon he quietly and surreptitiously allowed his trousers to fall down around his ankles and bared his arse to the young members of the congregation who always sat together in a group at one side of the pulpit. Speaking now of the infinite miseries of hell the old parson cried, "Old people look at it! Young people look at it!" The old folk wept at his invocation of hell's fire but, at the sight of his bare arse, the youngsters burst into laughter.

Collected in Carrickbroad, County Armagh.*

The Gaelic Catechist

After the stations in a country house the priest began to give out the catechism. He came to these two young lads and they hadn't a word of it, so they told him that they had learned the catechism in Irish and asked him if he could understand Irish, knowing full well that he could not. "Well," said the priest, "go ahead till I hear what it's like anyway." So they started off, but it was scolding him they were, only he didn't know it.

Collected in Moneygashel, Blacklion, County Cavan, in 1980.

The Sick Calls

The parish priest of Glenelly complained in his Sunday sermon that parishioners came with unneccessary sick calls which he had to attend to late at night. Recently he had been called from his bed on a wild, wintry night by a man who said his wife was so bad she "was for death". The man lived in an isolated, almost inaccessible glen, and the priest had to harness his pony into the trap to go to the place. After much delay and difficulty he eventually reached the house only to find the whole place in darkness. "And where was the man?" the priest called in frustration from the pulpit. "In bed with his wife, where I should have been!"

I have collected two versions of this tale, one in the 1950s in the Glenelly area of County Tyrone and the other from Glangevlin in County Cavan. Interestingly enough, both deal with aged parish priests and in both the priests are named.

Orange Hoors Don't Need to Know

When the priest met scholars – boys and girls attending primary school – it was the practice to put questions to them out of the catechism, and indeed priests sometimes questioned older people they met also. A priest new to the parish engaged in this practice with all and sundry. One day he met a man in his late twenties and recognised him as a Catholic when he raised his cap in greeting. What the priest did not know was that the fellow was rather dense. The priest spoke to him and said, "Now, what is the Mass?"

"Ah, I know what the Mass is, Father," said the young man.

"That's not the answer in the catechism," the priest shouted, losing his temper almost immediately.

"I know it's not."

"Then what is the Mass?"

"I know what the Mass is and that's good enough," said the other stubbornly.

"If you met Robert Turner," the priest queried, "if you met Robert Turner the Orangeman from Adavoyle, is that the answer you'd give him if he asked you what the Mass was?"

"It is not," said the fellow.

The priest persisted with his questions but could get no satisfaction. Suddenly he hit on an approach to get the fellow to answer. "You stand your ground," he told him. "I'll go back down the road a bit and turn and come back: but I'll not be the priest then, I'll be Robert Turner. If I ask you what the Mass is will you tell me?"

"Since you want it that way," said the fellow, "I will if I must."

The priest walked a short distance down the road, then turned and retraced his steps. When he came abreast of the young man he said, "Do you know me?"

"I suppose I do."

"Who am I?"

"You're Robert Turner."

"Right. Now tell me, what is the Mass?"

"Go to hell you Orange hoor you! What do you want to know for?"

I heard this tale from several storytellers in Dromantee, County Armagh, in the 1930s.

The Love Charm

In an age when people believed in the supernatural, charms and rituals were used to ward off evil influences or attract the spirits' blessing. Hallow Eve love charms, both simple and satanic in invocation and ritual, derived from the belief that on this night the air and atmosphere were alive with mystery and magic. The *Annals of the Four Masters* recorded that at Samhain hordes of demons came out of the Northern World to terrorise the countryside, and tradition tells us that this upheaval derived from the fairies who changed from the uplands to their lowland winter quarters on this night. These beliefs were reflected in the farming practice of "booleying" when livestock, moved to the hills to keep them from thieving in the growing period, were brought back after the late harvest to the land around the farmhouse.

Hallow Eve rituals could be benign or unsettling. One custom was to burn two nuts on the blade of an old shovel, representing a local boy and girl known to be courting. As the nuts heated they moved to and fro and the cries went up, "She's pulling away from him"; "He's following her"; "Now she's coming back". If the nuts caught fire and burnt out together the couple would marry; if they burned far apart from each other then the couples were fated to part. While such games were no more than harmless fun, other, more serious customs demanded nerve and courage. I heard tales told in my youth of attempts at divination; in one ritual, one had to riddle or sieve oats between two open doors in the name of the devil at midnight, when the person one would marry was to appear and take the sieve. A servant girl once practised it and her master appeared: she threw the sieve aside and ran into the house saying it was "all a cod". Her master was a married man, but his wife died suddenly and he did marry the girl, though he denied having appeared in the barn at Hallow Eve.

As well as magic and charms, there was also a belief in what people everywhere called "coax-ee-lorum" preparations; some claimed these could be bought in a druggists while others made herbal concoctions which could be dissolved in a drink or in food. Coax-ee-lorum was used to put the "come hither" on a person you fancied.

The Grass Mouse Charm

The grass mouse is not the same as the house mouse: he's a wee, wee fellow with a long tail on him. You had to catch him alive – of course it was a bit of cruelty – and you had an ordinary sticking pin, you drove it across through his two eyes, in and out the other side. When you went to the dance that night you stuck the mouse onto a lassie when you were dancing. Where you stuck it I don't know, you'd have a fierce difficult job, but you'd have her home with you as a result. She'd want to come home with you.

Collected in Blacklion, County Cavan. Incidentally, the field mouse, roasted or boiled into mouse soup, was the main ingredient in sundry folk cures and remedies, including even baldness in men.

It Takes the Biscuit

She lived up there at one side of Dowra in a place called Teebawn, and she was about sixty-five years of age or up to it, and she was still as proud and prim! This young fellow, a fine-looking lad, used to be codding her; telling her how much he loved her and how nice she was and how happy he'd be if he was married to her. It was all bluffing and pulling her leg, you know, and breaking his heart laughing at her.

Damn but she was coming out of Dowra this day and he met her. He had a creel of turf on his back and he was standing smoking his pipe. Oh, he told her how nice she looked and all that and asked, "Did you bring any sweets for me? God, if I had known you were going to Dowra I'd have been with you: I'd be happy walking the road with you."

"Well," she said, "I brought you a biscuit," and she handed it to him.

"I'll ate it when I'm done smoking," he said, putting the biscuit in his pocket, and he smoked away while he codded her, and then he turned for home.

When he got back to his house he had to fodder cattle and he had a lock of other outside jobs to do as well and as it came on a wet evening he got soaked. He decided to change his clothes and go down to Dowra and have a few pints. He went to get his pipe and tobacco and his knife out of the wet clothes, and matches of course, and he come at this biscuit. It was so wet 'twas in wee crumbs and he threw it out on the floor. One of the hens came in and started picking at the crumbs, and all of a sudden the hen leapt onto his knee and started to conoodle and crow up at him; chatting him, d'you know. He put the hen down but it jumped back up straight away. Anyway, he put out the hen and he struck out for Dowra, but begod the hen followed him and in the end he had to get a lend of a creel at a house and put the hen under it. He had his few pints in Dowra and on the way back he let the hen out of the creel and she followed him home. He put her in the hen-house and went off to bed himself. He slept sound after the pints but when he woke up next morning the hen was lying against his cheek at the pillow!

He had to get rid of the hen and, you see, if he had ate the biscuit he'd be after the woman the way the hen was after him.

That's the only mystical love potion that I heard about. But I found it out, I found it out now! A while after, the Teebawn woman was hired as a servant in a school-teacher's house down our way, in Cornagee. It wasn't far from us so I used to céilí in it, and with one chat and another I got on to her about the love charm. I asked her what it was and she told me she'd give me the secret if I'd bring her twenty Woodbine cigarettes: she was a devil for cigarettes. They were only a penny a packet at the time, a penny for five, so I brought her the twenty.

It was only a female could work the charm, she told me. The biscuit had to be tied under the left armpit for an hour and sweated on if possible; she could work about on it, but it had to be for the full hour. There was a certain incantation the woman had to repeat every minute, and she had to make sure not to miss one even though she might be working. Then any fellow that she'd have an eye about or that she had a crack in, she got him to ate the biscuit and he fell head over heels for her.

She told me the whole thing. I gave it to a few and they told me it was successful; but I charged them for it! I gave it to this pair of girls and they got married, got fellows that wouldn't have looked at them. They gave me a good few quid for that!

The end of the secret I won't tell you. It was brief, brief enough, but I don't want to make it broadcast. I didn't push the Teebawn woman where she got it. Them old pishogues be in a family for a hundred generations, and the family never let them out to the next-door neighbour.

Collected in Blacklion, County Cavan, in 1977.

The Charm of the Knife

A girl who wanted to find out who her husband might be decided to invoke a Hallow Eve ritual to divine her future. The ritual demanded that, in the name of the devil, the girl was to wash her shift at midnight in the waters where a stream dividing three townlands met. She was then to bring the shift home and set it to dry over the back of a chair on the hearth before the fire, and the man she was to marry would appear and turn the shift. She also had to leave a plate of the traditional Hallow Eve dish of champ or colcannon on the table. Champ was made up of mashed potatoes, milk and chopped greens with a well of melted butter in the centre, and the dish was eaten with a spoon, scraping around and outside and dipping each spoonful into the melted butter. The spoon was to be left on the table also, but this the girl forgot.

She was sitting at the fire when a young local man came in, tired and hungry after disporting himself – it seemed to her – by running off neighbours' carts. Immediately he came in the door he said he thought something was burning and he turned the shift at the fire. He asked about the champ and said he would take a bite, but as there was no spoon at the table he took out his clasp knife and used that instead. Then he left, leaving the girl disgusted at the failure of the charm because she knew the man well and knew he was soon to emigrate to America, which indeed he did.

However, during the following year she decided to emigrate herself and by chance she met the man again at a function in New York. After swopping some chat and enquiries about people at home she suddenly remembered the events of Hallow Eve and, opening her handbag, she took out the clasp knife which he had left behind on that night. She told him it was his and offered the knife to him. He grew serious and asked her where she had found it.

"Last Hallow Eve when you came to our house you ate the champ and left that on the table behind you," she told him.

"That was the night," he replied, "when I was at home in a dead faint for over an hour. I was never in your house." With that he caught up the knife and drove it into her, stabbed her to death.

Told to me in Carnanrancy, County Tyrone. A less grim version of this tale was written by Seán de Buitléar of Baile na nUan, An Gleann, County Wexford, in 1935, and is quoted in full in Séamas Ó Catháin's *Bedside Book of Irish Folklore*, Mercier, 1980.

Folklore and Folk Fact

In some folk-tales the storyteller would narrate the story in the first person, and in many instances it would be given as actual experience. Sometimes, too, the story would be woven around a noted local character, who would be invested with a fresh personality for each oncoming generation. Inevitably, then, many tales would become enlarged or exaggerated.

Folk belief also contained many fictions. My cousin, the late Oweny Quinn, was a hired servant boy in a farm in County Armagh where one of the servant girls got "into trouble". In a céilí house soon after, an aged, solemn citizen began to talk in a hushed voice of the girl and her predicament. "You young fellas like to boast," he said, "of getting your hand on the bird's nest. But that's not the most dangerous part of a woman: there's a hole below her navel like a dead pig's eye, and for your life never meddle with it!"

Misplaced beliefs could be cruel. In the Sperrin Mountains country of County Tyrone, the folk antidote for venereal disease was that, as well as taking a few herbal remedies, a man so infected had to have intercourse with a virgin: with this the disease would pass to the girl while the man would be cleansed. I was told that doctors in the local hospitals were at one time puzzled as to why so many physically or mentally retarded girls had to be treated for venereal disease. The assumption of the folk was that such girls would be virgins since their deformities or disabilities kept them outside the normal courtship associations.

She Grabbed the Saddle Horn

Two American soldiers who were stationed in the North during the Second World War cycled one night to a dance in a country hall in Cleenish, County Fermanagh. After the dance they left home two girls, each carrying his girl on the crossbar of his bike, a familiar way of travelling at that time. One of the soldiers, a black man, wanting a scud of a court with his partner, stopped and threw the bike against the ditch. Only then did the girl notice that it was in fact a woman's bike: one without a crossbar.

I heard this tale told around Blacklion by a few narrators who said it took place during the Second World War when American troops were billeted around Enniskillen. The title of the tale is from Vance Randolph's collection and I give it for a special reason: the tale is the only known instance in which an American folk-tale would appear to have reversed the process of distribution and crossed eastwards over the Atlantic, finding a provenance in Fermanagh.*

Pigs and Pork and Fast Women

A much talked about character in Dromantee parish, known as Paddy Bells, was the subject of several tales, some of which he told against himself, such as this tale of a time he butchered three pigs and sold them one Thursday in Newry pork market.

Fond of a drink, Paddy, with the payment in his pocket, made for a certain public house where discipline was never too strict: your sleep was not disturbed in the bar if you had too much bad drink taken. And to such an establishment went a class of woman whose moral standards (and not only in the sense of sexual morality) were questionable. All parishes throughout Ireland had their quota of such fast women, though admittedly few in number.

Three sisters from the far end of the parish saw Paddy go into the public house and, knowing that he had sold pork, followed him in. No ordinary country woman would then be seen in a pub of any kind, though she might take a half-one of whiskey or a glass of wine in a secretive snug, but on this occasion the whiskey flowed as Paddy treated the three sisters. Eventually, however, Paddy got drunk and fell asleep, and when he awoke the price of his three pigs had vanished.

He suspected the three sisters of relieving him of his money, but how could he be sure? He took the loss of the money in his philosophical way because, he explained, "I seen the three at second Mass the following Sunday in Dromantee chapel, and they marched up the middle aisle showing themselves off, with a pig apiece on their backs!"

She Would Only Marry a Good Mobber

There was this girl and she was very good with the tongue and no one was able for her, no one could mob her. So she said that she wouldn't marry a man only a man who would be able to mob her. There were three brothers lived not far from her; the two eldest were smart but the youngest lad was a bit of an *amadán*. The two lads thought they might have a chance with the girl and they headed off this day to see her, with the foolish fellow following behind them.

They weren't gone far when he started an awful meel-a-murder and calling, all excited, for them to come back. So the two lads went back and, ah, he had only found a duck egg. They gave him a hammering and told him to get back home, and then they started off again. They went on and when they had gone another bit the yelling started again, all the shouts and wonders of the world: the youngest lad had found a *cipín*, a short bit of stick. So they gave him another hammering and headed off again, but before they got to the girl's house there were still more roars and shouts. They turned to see the young lad come running with the half-full of his hat of ass's dung, so they gave him another belting and went on to the girl's house.

The *amadán* went on too and when he came to the house he pushed the door in, but there was no sign of anyone; they were above in the forrey or loft. He went in under the ladder to the loft and after some time the lassie came kicking the two boys down the stepladder, and the foolish fellow said, "You lift your leg very high, miss".

"Ah," she answered, "there's fire in me arse."

"Would you roast a duck egg on it?"

"You'd burn your finger turning it."

"I have a nice *cipín* here," said the *amadán*.

"Ah, shite," said she.

"Oh, the full of me hat of it!"

He was the only one able to answer her, so he got the girl.

Collected in Wheathill, County Fermanagh, from a storyteller who had heard it from his uncle, a Cavan man. Other variants are known and have been heard in a few counties.*

Immersed to Conceive

A local landlord badly wanted an heir but, though they had been married for a good many years, the couple were childless. One day an unseen watcher saw the landlord and his wife copulate beside the shores of Lough McNean, a large lake between County Cavan and County Fermanagh. The watcher wondered that they should be having sex there for the Big House was nearby. But immediately after the act of intercourse the landlord seized his wife and tossed her in her full attire into the chill waters of the lough. It was claimed that she became pregnant as a result of the water treatment as an heir was born to the couple nine months later.

Collected in Blacklion, County Cavan, in 1977. There is no traditional consensus of belief behind this practice, but in many parts of rural Ireland a cold water treatment was given to a cow which failed to conceive. Immediately after service from the bull a bucket of very cold water was dashed up along the cow's spine, and this was said to be effective.

The *Amadán* and the Handy Woman

There was a fellow something like that lug of a fellow in your story ["The Obedient Son"], a sort of a half-boiled eejit of a fellow who knew sweet bugger all about women or anything else. He didn't know how to catch a girl and there was only himself and his ould mother in it – the father was dead – until this day the mother said she thought it was time he was looking for a woman for he was getting on in years and pretty soon no one would take him.

"Ah, but mother dear," he said, "I want no one but you. I know nothing about a woman; I don't know what to do with a woman."

"You don't need to know," said his mother. "She'll know and if she doesn't you'll damn soon find out."

So away she took him with her this night to a house where she thought there was a likely enough girl that might take him, and they were made welcome and then the bargaining started and the match was made, and they were soon married.

Well, the night they were married the mother put him to bed with the new woman in a room of their own. The next morning he was up gay and early before the new wife and when he came down to the kitchen his mother was there on the floor before him waiting to see how he had got on. "Well," she said, "did you do all I told you?"

"Do be damned," said he, "I only done middlin' well. She's no good," he continued, "no good at all. She done nothing all night only sleep and sleep away, and me duntin' and duntin' and never took a fidge out of her. She wouldn't speak or nothin'. I'll not sleep with her again; if you won't have me I'll get a bed on my own and lie in it."

"Damn the sweet fear of you," said the mother.

"Ah, now," said the *amadán*, "I had poor luck after all. It's all your fault," he goes on, "she's not made the way you said at all." And the poor eejit got himself into such a fury over it after all his mother had said about the girl that he was for packing a few things in a bag and leaving the house altogether. The mother seen he was in earnest and told him to hang on a while till she'd see was there anything wrong, and she went down to the bed where the new woman was, whipped back the bedclothes and made her strip naked, into the bloody pelt, and of course she was just like any other woman. The mother called the *amadán* of a son and she said, "I see nothing out of shape with her".

"Oh, God take care of us," said the *amadán*, looking at his wife's twat. "I never went near them far lands at all!"

So they went to bed again that night and seemed to get on all right and things were going well, but coming on winter a year or so later the old mother got a bad cold and didn't come over it and died. The son was very vexed [sad] and moped at the fire for three months and was always at her grave every chance he got, and his wife got little good of him and started to scold him for the way he was carrying on. That riz the *amadán* in him and he got mad with the wife and started to give her a helluva sore time; she had no living at all.

There was another old woman living across the fields and she had an idea what was wrong between them from the first – he was an eejit, do you see – and she used to listen to them arguing and calling other for this and for that [recriminating]. This day when she got him away to a fair the old woman crossed over to the wife. "Is it possible," she asked, "that this man of yours is giving you such a bad time? You've failed away to scrapings."

"It's true," said the girl, "it's because there's no family."

"How long is this you're married now?"

"Two years and over," said the girl. "I don't know what I'll do at all. I don't think I can stay with him much longer."

"Don't say that," pleaded the old woman.

The wife began to cry. "I can't endure it."

"Oh dear," said the old woman, "if it's as bad as that we must do something."

"I don't know under God what anyone can do," said the wife.

"Well I'll tell you what to do," said the woman. "Get a right, tight wee bundle and shove it up well under your petticoat and gradually make yourself twice as big as you used to be. And when James comes home" – that was the *amadán*'s name; the old woman knew how to handle his sort, as you'll see – "when James comes home I'll drop over."

So in the end the girl done what the old woman told her, and when James came home she was going about the kitchen doing this and that turn and her damn near twice as big looking as she used to be. James was eyeing her up and down but said nothing. The old woman came in presently and let on to ask how the market prices and the fair was. And then she said, nice and easy, to James, "I'm glad to see the way things is thriving with you at last".

"How do you mean?" said James.

"I see you have the woman in the family way."

"Damn but if it's not out of time. Is that why she's so full of herself like that?"

The old woman said it was and, man alive, he was in great glee with himself now, and when the woman left for home he conveyed her over the fields, in great heart altogether, laughing and humming.

"Now James," said the old woman, "as soon as your woman is ready for the wisp[1] run like hell for me. Don't delay one second; run over and give me a shout whether it's night or day." She was what they called a handy woman, before doctors or midwives were ever heard of in this part of the country.

The *amadán* was as busy now as two or three eating the one herring: working in the fields, making ditches, cleaning the house. When the old woman got him away working in the bog she slipped over to the girl and put the next part of her plan before her. The girl was afraid of her life that James would find out that it was all a cram, but the old woman told her not to worry and leave all to her. So no later than a few nights after that the girl took bad; shouting and bawling and taking the lime off the walls, she was that bad. James didn't take time even to pull on his shirt or boots and he run the way he was over the fields in the dark, damn near the way he came into the world.

"Lord, Lord, come quick!" he shouted, kicking the old woman's door. "Thon woman of mine is taking the lime off the walls. She's either mad or dying!"

"Away you go," shouted the old woman from the window, "and throw something on you; stick your feet in some ould pair of boots and pull a shirt over your head and don't catch your death of cold. Away and hurry and knock them up in the public house and get a bottle of whiskey, and delay no time till you're back. You might have to go somewhere else to help me as well."

Away James goes doing what she bid him do. Half light in the head he stuck his feet in his boots, pulled on a shirt and coat and trousers, and away like the devil spinning heather for the whiskey.

The old woman was through the door as soon as he took the light out of it – she was ready waiting at home for all this to happen – and in she goes to her own hen-house where she had the fattest hen picked out for the job. She wrings its neck and lets the blood out of it; takes it up, plucks it as clean as the heart of your hand, and then she gets a nice wee border cap she'd been making all along, and a tidy wee coat and a wee shawl, and she dresses the hen up the best you've ever seen. Well, I don't know if you've ever noticed, but an old hen's arse is very fat and stuck-out like. The old woman fixed the hat just above that and away like hell with her over the fields to James's house. She was on the floor with this hen in clothes in her arms when James gets back and the sweat running off him like rain, and she was hush-a-baain' [rocking it in her arms] when he comes in, and he laughing and ca-heein' [whooping] and half drunk already.

"Well, James, a fine braw son for you," she said to him.

He let another ca-hee out of him and ran over, and she thought he would ate it the way he was kissing and slapping the hen on the arse under the wee hat. He got real stocious drunk – the old woman knew he would once he got his lips on the whiskey – and he lay down on the cooltee [*cúl tí*] bed in the kitchen and went dead to the world asleep.

The old woman let him sleep, but when he wakened and wanted to see his son she said, "James, avick, I'm very sorry for your trouble. I'm sorry to tell you your son is dead and buried: me and your neighbour buried it afore daylight. You may thank yourself for that, James," she went on, wicked like, "it's the bad living and hard time you've given your wife is the cause of this. Let you be more than careful in future how you treat your woman. Be kinder to her, or not one of your children will live."

The truth was, and the old woman knew it, that the girl couldn't have children, but you couldn't explain that to an *amadán* like James. But after the old woman had spoke her mind he wasn't a bad man at all and they lived in peace and happiness till the notion of children went clean out of his head.

[1]Refers to the custom of placing a woman in labour on a straw bed on the floor. Collected in Muninameale, Greencastle, County Tyrone.*

The Coarse Doctor

A young man contracted venereal disease, an ailment he did not understand, so he went to consult the doctor one evening. The doctor was out walking when he called so he waited in the surgery and in a while the doctor strolled in, swinging his umbrella. Although he was very popular, the doctor had a bad habit of giving short grunts when he was displeased, though his sense of humour had never been known to desert him. When the young man explained his trouble the doctor grunted and said, "Throw it out there".

The young man exposed his penis and shyly asked, "What's wrong with it, doctor?"

"You put that," retorted the doctor, "where I wouldn't put the end of my umbrella!"

Another time the doctor was called by a grandmother to attend her grand-daughter who was ill with pains. He examined the girl and returned to the kitchen. The old woman recounted all the folk remedies she had tried on the girl and added, "I even gave her dandelion, doctor".

"No good," he grunted, "she got dandy standing."

The girl was pregnant.

A young man from Clontigrea had another story. "I was with that doctor," he said, "and he must be the coarsest man in Ireland. He put me down on a couch and grabbed me and the light left me eyes. He said, 'When did your bowels move?'

"It's near a week," I told him.

"'Go home then and take a pound of salts,' said he, 'for there's mountains of shite in you!'"

These anecdotes were told about a certain doctor in Dromantee, County Armagh.*

The Naked Truth

Naked humanity outside the bed chamber was, and is, considered bawdy, but the amusement, laughter or indignation generated depends on the character of the incident and the degree of nudity involved. Amusement in its mildest form is provoked by accidental nudity, and when tales of this type are told they bring an indulgent chuckle or a guilty smirk. Much more serious though is the case where nakedness is imposed, and imposed as a punishment on one of the community. The term "community" is perhaps too weak a word to denote such an action – "tribe" is more appropriate – and its object is to ridicule and belittle.

The Naked Custom

Until two or three decades ago the dresser was the pride of every country woman's house, and pride of place on the dresser was given to an array of willow-patterned plates, especially the oblong plates on the top shelf known as "Christmas plates" which were only taken out for special occasions.

In the Glens of Antrim an anxious neighbour called to just such a house one morning at daybreak: the cow was calving and he needed help. The woman of the house got up and walked, still half asleep, into the kitchen. Like the élite of Europe at one time, she slept in the bare buff, and before opening the door to the voice calling outside she reached to the top shelf of the dresser for a broad Christmas plate to protect her modesty. She held the plate in position over her crotch as she opened the door and as she turned, once the message was delivered, she turned and switched it quickly to her backside!

Told to me in Cushendall, County Antrim, in the 1950s.

Exposure in Chicago

Tom Murphy was a wonderful storyteller in Chicago, and he was telling this night how there was an Irish girl went to work out in the States, and she was out walking one very hot, sunny day. She was very warm but she saw a lovely pool of water or a lake and she thought she'd go for a swim. She didn't have a swimsuit naturally but there was no one around, not a soul; she was in a very quiet place out in the country. So she stripped and got in the water, but after she had been in a while she heard a shout: "Come out, you're trespassing! Get out of there!" There was a man on the bank above her.

She saw a roasting pan in the water; it was about a foot and a half long and she got the handle of it, pulled it up and she held it up in front of her. She stood up, in the water, holding the pan, and she said to the man who disturbed her, "Do you know what I think of you?"

"I don't know what you think of me," he answered her, "but I do know that you think there's a bottom on that pan!"

Collected in Carricknagavna, Mullabawn, County Armagh, in 1983. The story was heard in Chicago.

The Black Patch

Old Sandy Nixon of Killyglassan, when the apples would start to get ripe in his orchard he watched them like a cat, and he had strings fixed from the trees into the house where he had an old bell fixed on some contraption so that if the trees was shook at all he'd know. He kept a loaded shotgun handy to thwart marauders robbing his orchard.

These two lassies, a big lassie called Belle and a cousin of hers who came to visit her, they went to bed one very hot night and they couldn't sleep. They were in their pelts with the heat and in the middle of the night, not able to sleep, they proposed they'd go and steal Sandy Nixon's apples. They got out of bed and put old shoes on their feet, two old hats on their heads, and covered themselves just with short jackets, and that's all they had on them it was such a melting hot night. They went and got a bag and made a hole in the hedge to get into the orchard. Belle climbed up a tree to give it a shake while the other lassie stayed below with the bag.

Belle gave the tree a shake and it was like a wee rattle of thunder, the big apples hitting the hard ground. With that the door of the house opened and old Sandy dashed out and down for the orchard. The other lassie dropped the bag and made out through the hole in the hedge. But Belle was above in the tree and it took her a good while clambering down from one branch to another till she got low enough, and then she slid down the branch and down on the ground. Sandy was within a yard of her when she dropped down beside him. She turned and ran and he shouted after her, "Stand your ground, Tom Todd! I know you anyway with the black patch on your trousers".

There was an old fellow, a tramp, working a week anywhere he would get work, and at the time he was working with a neighbouring farmer for a couple of weeks. This Tom Todd wore white corduroys with a black triangular patch on the fork, and when Sandy seen the black patch on Belle he thought it was this tramp. Old Sandy's eyes weren't perfect, and he summonsed Todd, summonsed him to court and swore it was him robbing the orchard. And Todd got fined and was damn near going to jail.

Collected in Moneygashel, Blacklion, County Cavan, in 1979.

A Naked Crucifixion

A local man in the parish of Killinagh was accused of having an adulterous affair with his sister-in-law whose husband was away in a mental hospital. A group of young local men decided to take action: some were for shooting the culprit outright but others insisted on a less violent punishment, and public exposure was decided on as the remedy. Late one Saturday night they caught the man, stripped him naked and tied him to a tree, his feet bound and arms outstretched on the branches as if crucified. Parishioners going to Killinagh Roman Catholic church on Sunday saw him hanging there on their way to Mass, but few stopped to stare and the women hurried by with downcast eyes. However, the priest was told and he ordered that the man be released forthwith.

The priest's denunciation of the act disturbed some of the young men, but others in the group were not satisfied that the man had been fully punished. In the end they decided to consult a local schoolmaster, then retired. This man, like others of his calling throughout Ireland in that era, had come directly or indirectly under the influence of the hedge schoolmasters who loved polysyllabic and sonorous speech – pompous, perhaps, but euphonious. The schoolmaster's verdict on the case is quoted by storytellers around the Blacklion area to this day. He advised:

"The person or persons concerned in the act deserve an abundant amount of credit for abstaining from staining the country's peaceful character with the ignoble blood of the viper."

Several storytellers around Blacklion fleshed out this account in recordings made in the 1970s.*

The Emergency Man

In the parish of Killinagh in County Cavan an emergency man occupied a farm, about six miles from Blacklion, from which the tenants had been evicted. The emergency man, sometimes corrupted to "melgerry man", was the term given to someone brought in from a strange district to occupy a farm from which the landlord had evicted the tenant. In the land wars masterminded by Michael Davitt such farms were boycotted, and no local men would take them over to graze or crop. The rural people detested the emergency man but he was supported by the landlord and also had protection from armed police, who were required, if called upon, to sleep on the occupied premises. The police claimed that they detested this duty, most of them being of rural stock themselves, and they were relieved when the menace of local opposition had subsided to a level that permitted the withdrawal of the armed guard. The emergency man was, however, permitted to carry a loaded revolver at all times.

The emergency man in Killinagh was on his way to Blacklion for foodstuffs and supplies when, on a very desolate part of the road, he saw four girls in their late teens or early twenties approaching. They seemed in high spirits and he sensed no danger from them, but when they came abreast of him they leaped suddenly and felled him to the road: they were in fact four young men in female attire. In the struggle the emergency man got the revolver out of his pocket but they managed to seize the weapon. They stripped him naked, put his clothes on the ditch with the revolver and some whiskey they had found in his possession on top. Then they bound his hands securely behind his back and tied a small "Sinn Fein flag" – an orange, white and green flag – on his penis.

The emergency man feared to go back home and walked on towards Blacklion. When anyone spotted him, especially the women, they concealed themselves, and no one heeded his cries for help. He walked the five or six miles to Blacklion where he went to the local magistrate's house and demanded that he be unbound and given clothes, but the magistrate refused (and as a result was dismissed from his post on the bench). There was no police barracks in Blacklion so the emergency man was compelled to walk the most of a further mile to the barracks in Belcoo. A constable was sent to retrieve his clothes and personal belongings which were found as they had been left on the ditch, together with the whiskey and the revolver. The emergency man never returned to the evicted farm, and soon disappeared from the district.*

Index

Index of Tale Types

The references are to Antti Aarne and Stith Thompson *The Types of the Folk-Tale*, Helsinki 1961 (F.F. Communications No. 184).

TYPE NO.

Index of Motifs

The references are to Stith Thompson *Motif-Index of Folk-Literature*, Bloomington, Indiana 1955–58 (6vols).

MOTIF

Alice Taylor
To School Through the Fields

Alice Taylor
An Irish Country Diary

Alice Taylor
Close to the Earth:
Poems of Country Life

In these poems Alice Taylor writes about country life and people with the same feeling and charm as she brought to the description of her childhood in *To School Through the Fields*.

D.P. Gee
Hotel at the Edge of the World

An Englishman is cast upon the mercies of Irish life in a small fishing town in the wild, wet west. Here he tries to come to terms with his supposed role as manager of an ancient hotel which he has unenthusiastically inherited.

Lacking the true British grit of a Basil Fawlty, he soon succumbs to the logic-defying charms of his new home as this hilarious novel charts his erratic progress through a colourful year.

Born in Portsmouth in 1930, D.P. Gee has been at sea since the age of sixteen. A sea pilot for fourteen years, he took a break from marine endeavours and bought a small hotel in Ireland, where his proprietorship did not survive recession.